# Dimensions Math
# Workbook 5B

## Authors and Reviewers

Jenny Kempe

Bill Jackson

Tricia Salerno

Allison Coates

Cassandra Turner

Singapore Math Inc.

## Published by Singapore Math Inc.

19535 SW 129th Avenue
Tualatin, OR 97062
www.singaporemath.com

Dimensions Math® Workbook 5B
ISBN 978-1-947226-27-2

First published 2020
Reprinted 2020, 2021 (twice)

Printed in China

## Acknowledgments

Editing by the Singapore Math Inc. team.
Design and illustration by Cameron Wray with Carli Bartlett.

# Contents

| Chapter | Exercise | Page |
|---|---|---|

| Chapter | Exercise | Page |
|---|---|---|

This workbook includes **Basics**, **Practice**, **Challenge**, and **Check** sections to review and deepen math skills.

BLANK

# Chapter 9 Decimals

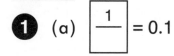

## Basics

**1** (a) $\boxed{\dfrac{1}{\phantom{xx}}}$ = 0.1

   (b) $\boxed{\dfrac{\phantom{xx}}{\phantom{xx}}}$ = 0.01

   (c) $\boxed{\dfrac{\phantom{xxx}}{\phantom{xxx}}}$ = 0.001

**2**

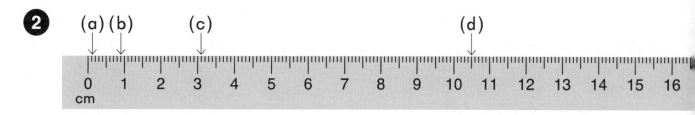

   (a) 1 mm = $\boxed{\dfrac{\phantom{xx}}{1{,}000}}$ m = 0.001 m

   (b) Express 9 mm in meters as a decimal.

   (c) Express 31 mm in meters as a decimal.

   (d) Express 105 mm in meters as a decimal.

**3** Express $\dfrac{3}{25}$ as a decimal.

$\dfrac{3}{25}$ = $\boxed{\dfrac{\phantom{xx}}{100}}$ = $\boxed{\phantom{xxxxxxxx}}$

**4** (a) Express $\frac{1}{8}$ as a decimal.

$$\frac{1}{8} = \boxed{\frac{\phantom{000}}{1,000}} = \boxed{\phantom{0000}}$$

(b) Express $5\frac{3}{8}$ as a decimal.

$$5\frac{3}{8} = 5\boxed{\frac{\phantom{000}}{1,000}} = \boxed{\phantom{0000}}$$

**5** Express 0.052 as a fraction in simplest form.

$$0.052 = \boxed{\frac{\phantom{000}}{1,000}} = \boxed{\frac{\phantom{00}}{\phantom{00}}}$$

**6** Express 3.135 as a mixed number in simplest form.

$$3.135 = 3\boxed{\frac{\phantom{000}}{1,000}} = 3\boxed{\frac{\phantom{00}}{\phantom{00}}}$$

## Practice

**7** Express each decimal as a fraction or mixed number.

(a) 0.09

(b) 0.11

(c) 0.407

(d) 0.003

(e) 8.23

(f) 11.017

**8** Circle the two decimals below that are equal.

0.32          0.032          3.2          0.320          32.0

**9** Express each of the following measurements as a decimal.

(a) 987 mm = [       ] m

(b) 42 mL = [       ] L

(c) 60 g = [       ] kg

(d) 3 m = [       ] km

**10** Express each fraction or mixed number as a decimal.

(a) $\dfrac{147}{1,000}$

(b) $3\dfrac{3}{50}$

(c) $6\dfrac{2}{5}$

(d) $20\dfrac{7}{8}$

(e) $6\dfrac{9}{40}$

(f) $1\dfrac{93}{200}$

**11** Express each decimal as a fraction or mixed number in simplest form.

(a) 0.48

(b) 1.65

(c) 0.002

(d) 8.075

(e) 1.408

(f) 3.625

# Challenge

**12** Label each arrow with a decimal.

**(a)**

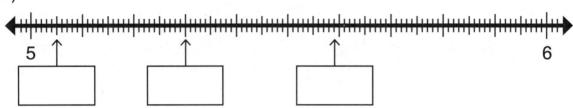

**(b)**

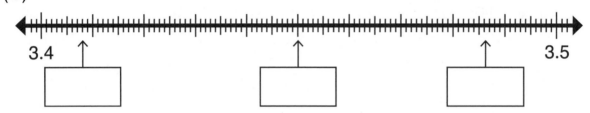

**(c)**

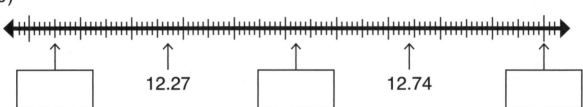

**(d)**

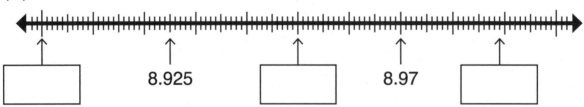

**(e)**

## Basics

**1** (a) $\boxed{\dfrac{1}{\phantom{-}}}$ of 1 = 0.1

(b) $\frac{1}{10}$ of $\frac{1}{10}$ = $\boxed{\dfrac{1}{\phantom{---}}}$ = 0.01

(c) $\frac{1}{10}$ of $\frac{1}{10}$ of $\frac{1}{10}$ = $\boxed{\dfrac{1}{\phantom{--}}}$ = 0.001

**2** Fill in the blanks with whole numbers or decimals.

(a)

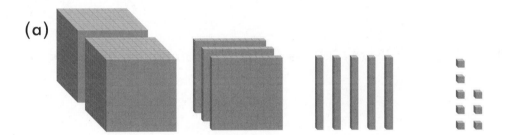

| Ones | Tenths | Hundredths | Thousandths |
|------|--------|------------|-------------|
| • | | | |

$\uparrow$      $\uparrow$      $\uparrow$      $\uparrow$

$\boxed{\phantom{0}}$ × 1     $\boxed{\phantom{0}}$ × 0.1     $\boxed{\phantom{0}}$ × 0.01    8 × $\boxed{\phantom{00}}$

(b) The decimal represented by the blocks is _____.

(c) The digit _____ is in the _____ place. Its value is 0.3.

(d) The digit _____ is in the hundredths place. Its value is _____.

(e) The digit _____ is in the thousandths place. Its value is _____.

(f) 2 + 0.3 + 0.05 + 0.008 = $\boxed{\phantom{0000}}$

**3** (a) Complete the chart.

| 10 10 10 10 10 10 10 | 1 1 1 1 1 | | 0.01 0.01 0.01 0.01 | 0.001 0.001 0.001 0.001 0.001 0.001 0.001 0.001 0.001 |
|---|---|---|---|---|

| Tens | Ones | Tenths | Hundredths | Thousandths |
|---|---|---|---|---|
| | | • | | |

(b) Write the number in expanded form.

(c) Write the number that is 0.001 more than the number on the chart.

(d) Write the number that is 0.1 less than the number on the chart.

**4** Complete the number patterns.

(a)

| 3.047 | 3.048 | | | |
|---|---|---|---|---|

(b)

| 10.202 | | 10.198 | | |
|---|---|---|---|---|

**5** Express the sum as a decimal.

(a) $10 + 6 + \frac{7}{10} + \frac{9}{100} + \frac{5}{1,000} = $ ☐

(b) $2 + 0.4 + 0.006 = $ ☐

(c) $8 + 0.05 + 0.009 = $ ☐

## Practice

**6** Use the number 98.958 to answer the following problems.

(a) The value of the digit in the hundredths place is _____.

(b) The value of the digit in the ones place is _____ times the value of the digit in the thousandths place.

(c) The digit with a value of 0.9 is in the _____ place.

(d) Write the number in expanded form.

**7** Write the numbers in expanded form.

(a) 0.092

(b) 12.007

(c) 401.206

**8** Write the decimal.

(a) $\frac{6}{100} + 3 + \frac{5}{1,000} + \frac{1}{10} = \boxed{\phantom{xxxx}}$

(b) $\frac{2}{1,000} + 4 + \frac{3}{10} = \boxed{\phantom{xxxx}}$

(c) $0.004 + \boxed{\phantom{xxxx}} + 90 + 1 = 91.304$

(d) $80 + 0.3 + \boxed{\phantom{xxxx}} + 0.006 = 80.326$

**9** (a) 0.999 + 0.001 = ☐      (b) 1 − 0.001 = ☐

(c) 0.006 + 0.004 = ☐      (d) 0.1 − 0.001 = ☐

(e) 0.13 − 0.001 = ☐      (f) 7.009 + 0.001 = ☐

## Challenge

**10** Complete the number pattern.

| 3 | ☐ | ☐ | ☐ | ☐ | → |

→ | 3.02 | ☐ | ☐ | 3.032 | ☐ |

**11** Study the number pattern.

2.985, 2.99, 2.995, ... 3.04

List all the numbers in the pattern between 2.995 and 3.04.

**12** Complete the fraction and write the decimal.

$\frac{1}{10}$ of $\frac{1}{10}$ of $\frac{1}{10}$ of $\frac{1}{10}$ = $\frac{1}{\boxed{\phantom{00}}}$ = ☐

## Basics

**1** Write > or < in each ◯.

(a)

| Ones | Tenths | Hundredths | Thousandths |
|------|--------|------------|-------------|
| 6    | 3      | 1          | 9           |
| 6    | 3      | 1          | 2           |

9 thousandths ◯ 2 thousandths

6.319 ◯ 6.312

(b)

| Ones | Tenths | Hundredths | Thousandths |
|------|--------|------------|-------------|
| 4    | 0      | 7          | 2           |
| 4    | 0      | 7          |             |

2 thousandths ◯ 0 thousandths

4.072 ◯ 4.07

(c)

| Ones | Tenths | Hundredths | Thousandths |
|------|--------|------------|-------------|
| 9    | 1      | 5          | 3           |
| 9    | 1      | 6          |             |

5 hundredths ◯ 6 hundredths

9.153 ◯ 9.16

**2** Label the numbers 6.455, 6.484, 6.408, 6.43, 6.445, and 6.48 on the number line below. Then write them in order from least to greatest.

6.4                                                                6.5

| | | | | | |
|---|---|---|---|---|---|
| | | | | | |

## Practice

**3** Write >, <, or = in each ◯.

(a)  1.514 ◯ 1.72

(b)  0.064 ◯ 0.64

(c)  8.2 ◯ 8.126

(d)  5.32 ◯ 5.320

(e)  0.041 ◯ $\frac{41}{100}$

(f)  $2\frac{10}{1,000}$ ◯ 2.002

**4** Circle the greatest decimal and cross off the least decimal.

0.325          0.35          0.053          0.53          0.32          0.532

**5** Write the numbers in increasing order.

(a)  7.41, 7.04, 4.704, 7.047

(b)  0.69, 6.89, 0.968, 6.986

(c)  14.64, 1.464, 4.641, 1.646

**6** Draw a path through the maze from the least number to the greatest number. The path should pass through all of the hexagons, but never go through the same hexagon more than once.

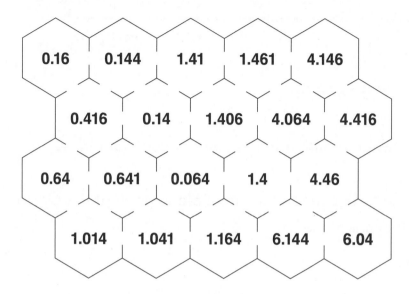

## Challenge

**7** Use the decimal point and each of the digits 6, 3, 2, and 0 only once in each number to write 6 numbers that are less than 1. List them in order from least to greatest.

**8** Use the decimal point and each of the digits 1, 2, 3, and 4 only once in each number to write as many decimal numbers between 4 and 14 as possible. List them in order from least to greatest.

## Basics

**1**

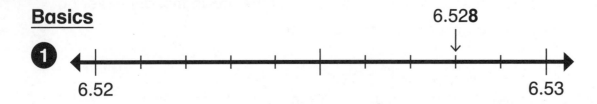

(a) Is 6.528 closer to 6.52 or 6.53?

(b) 6.528 is _____ when rounded to the second decimal place.

(c) To round a number to the second decimal place, look at the digit in the _____ decimal place.

**2**

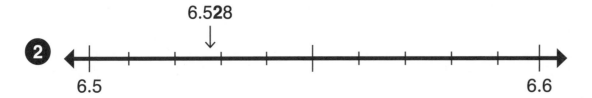

(a) Is 6.528 closer to 6.5 or 6.6?

(b) 6.528 is _____ when rounded to the first decimal place.

(c) To round to the first decimal place, look at the digit in the _____ decimal place. If it is less than _____, round down.

**3**

(a) 6.528 is _____ when rounded to a whole number.

(b) To round to a whole number, look at the digit in the _____ decimal place. If it is _____ or greater, round up.

**4** Circle the statement below that shows that 2.014 was rounded to the first decimal place, and not to a whole number.

2.014 ≈ 2                    2.014 ≈ 2.0                    2.014 ≈ 2.00

**5** Circle the statement below that shows that 10.004 was rounded to the second decimal place, and not to the first decimal place or a whole number.

10.004 ≈ 10                    10.004 ≈ 10.0                    10.004 ≈ 10.00

## Practice

**6** Answer the questions below using the given decimals above the number line.

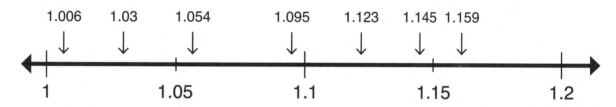

(a)  Which decimals are 1 when rounded to a whole number?

(b)  Which decimals are 1.0 when rounded to the first decimal place?

(c)  Which decimals are 1.1 when rounded to the first decimal place?

(d)  Which decimals are 1.15 when rounded to the second decimal place?

**7** Round each decimal to the second decimal place, to the first decimal place, and to a whole number.

| Decimal | Second Decimal Place | First Decimal Place | Whole Number |
|---|---|---|---|
| 9.285 | | | |
| 29.761 | | | |
| 0.647 | | | |
| 32.253 | | | |
| 13.604 | | | |
| 9.007 | | | |
| 6.995 | | | |

## Challenge

**8** Write the least and greatest possible numbers with 3 decimal places and a digit greater than 0 in the thousandths place that are:

(a) 3.48 when rounded to the second decimal place.

Least:                          Greatest:

(b) 7.7 when rounded to the first decimal place.

Least:                          Greatest:

(c) 12 when rounded to a whole number.

Least:                          Greatest:

## Check

**1** Use the number 9,200.029 to answer the following problems.

(a) The value of the digit in the thousandths place is _____.

(b) The digit with a value of 0.02 is in the _____ place.

(c) Write the number in expanded form.

(d) 1 thousand more than this number is _____.

(e) 1 thousandth more than this number is _____.

(f) 1 ten less than this number is _____.

(g) 1 tenth less than this number is _____.

**2** Write >, <, or = in each $\bigcirc$.

(a) $5.904 \bigcirc 5 + 0.004 + \frac{90}{100}$

(b) $8 + 0.9 + 0.04 + 0.009 \bigcirc 0.008 + 7 + 0.05 + 0.1$

(c) $0.06 + 3 + 0.1 + 0.007 \bigcirc 3 + 0.006 + 0.06$

(d) $10 + 6 + \frac{7}{10} + \frac{9}{100} + \frac{5}{1,000} \bigcirc 10 + 6 + \frac{90}{100} + \frac{5}{1,000}$

(e) $3 + 0.2 + 0.006 \bigcirc \frac{6}{100} + 3 + \frac{2}{1,000}$

**3** Express each value as a decimal.

(a) $\frac{3}{25}$

(b) $7\frac{9}{200}$

(c) $\frac{5}{8}$

(d) $10\frac{7}{40}$

(e) $\frac{37}{4}$

(f) $\frac{45}{8}$

(g) $1 + \frac{1}{5} + \frac{1}{20} + \frac{1}{250}$

(h) $2 + \frac{1}{2} + \frac{7}{125}$

**4** Express each value as a fraction or mixed number in simplest form.

(a) 0.14

(b) 8.320

(c) 2.008

(d) 0.145

(e) 4.875

(f) 1.275

**5** Write the numbers in increasing order.

(a) 0.409, 0.049, 0.044, 0.49, 0.4

(b) 4.386, 4.683, 4.638, 4.68

(c) $6\frac{1}{4}$, $\frac{6,521}{1,000}$, 6.215, $6\frac{63}{250}$

**6** Round each decimal to the second decimal place, to the first decimal place, and to a whole number.

| Decimal | Second Decimal Place | First Decimal Place | Whole Number |
|---------|----------------------|---------------------|--------------|
| 0.785   |                      |                     |              |
| 8.058   |                      |                     |              |
| 5.994   |                      |                     |              |
| 42.899  |                      |                     |              |
| 199.902 |                      |                     |              |

## Challenge

**7** Use the decimal point and any of the digits 3, 4, 5, and 6. Write all the numbers with up to 3 decimal places that round to 6.5 when rounded to the first decimal place. The digits can be used more than once.

## Basics

**1** (a)

0.324    [   ]    [   ]    [   ]

(b)  $0.324 \times 10 \times 10 = 0.324 \times 100 =$ [   ]

(c)  $0.324 \times 10 \times 10 \times 10 = 0.324 \times$ [   ] $=$ [   ]

(d)  $3.24 \times 100 =$ [   ]

**2**  Complete the charts and fill in the blanks.

(a)

| Hundreds | Tens | Ones | Tenths | Hundredths | Thousandths |
|---|---|---|---|---|---|
|  |  | 3 | 4 | 1 | 2 |
|  |  |  |  |  |  |

× 10

$3 . 4\ 1\ 2 \times 10 =$ [   ]

(b)

| Hundreds | Tens | Ones | Tenths | Hundredths | Thousandths |
|---|---|---|---|---|---|
|  |  | 2 | 7 | 0 | 1 |
|  |  |  |  |  |  |

× 100

$2 . 7\ 0\ 1 \times 100 =$ [   ]

(c)

| Hundreds | Tens | Ones | Tenths | Hundredths | Thousandths |
|---|---|---|---|---|---|
|  |  | 0 | 1 | 6 | 4 |
|  |  |  |  |  |  |

× 1,000

0 . 1 6 4 × 1,000 = [    ]

(d)

| Hundreds | Tens | Ones | Tenths | Hundredths | Thousandths |
|---|---|---|---|---|---|
|  |  | 0 | 1 | 9 |  |
|  |  |  |  |  |  |

× 1,000

0 . 1 9 0 × 1,000 = [    ]

## Practice

**3** (a) 0.01 × 10 = [    ]  (b) 0.001 × 10 = [    ]

(c) 6.094 × 10 = [    ]  (d) 10 × 55.7 = [    ]

**4** (a) 0.01 × 100 = [    ]  (b) 0.001 × 100 = [    ]

(c) 6.094 × 100 = [    ]  (d) 100 × 55.7 = [    ]

**5** (a) $0.01 \times 1,000 =$ ☐  (b) $0.001 \times 1,000 =$ ☐

(c) $6.094 \times 1,000 =$ ☐  (d) $1,000 \times 55.7 =$ ☐

**6** (a) $0.17 \times 1,000 =$ ☐  (b) $10 \times 89.2 =$ ☐

(c) $2.391 \times 100 =$ ☐  (d) $100 \times 98.05 =$ ☐

(e) $1,000 \times 0.43 =$ ☐  (f) $23.942 \times 10 =$ ☐

**7** (a) $3.73 \times$ ☐ $= 37.3$  (b) $0.709 \times$ ☐ $= 709$

(c) ☐ $\times 0.051 = 51$  (d) $10 \times$ ☐ $= 209.4$

(e) ☐ $\times 100 = 80$  (f) ☐ $\times 9.86 = 9,860$

## Challenge

**8** (a) $0.004 \times 10,000 =$ ☐  (b) $0.621 \times 100,000 =$ ☐

(c) $0.0008 \times$ ☐ $= 0.08$  (d) $10,000 \times$ ☐ $= 92$

## Basics

 (a)

| 100 | 10 | 1 | | ÷ 10 → | 10 | 1 | 0.1 | | ÷ 10 → | 1 | 0.1 | 0.01 | | ÷ 10 → | 0.1 | 0.01 | 0.001 |

324

(b)  324 ÷ 10 = ☐

(c)  324 ÷ 10 ÷ 10 = 324 ÷ 100 = ☐

(d)  324 ÷ 10 ÷ 10 ÷ 10 = 324 ÷ ☐ = ☐

2  Complete the charts and fill in the blanks.

(a)

| Hundreds | Tens | Ones | Tenths | Hundredths | Thousandths |
|----------|------|------|--------|------------|-------------|
|          |      | 8    | 3      | 2          |             |
|          |      |      |        |            |             |

÷ 10

8 . 3  2  ÷ 10 = ☐

(b)

| Hundreds | Tens | Ones | Tenths | Hundredths | Thousandths |
|----------|------|------|--------|------------|-------------|
| 1        | 4    | 2    | 7      |            |             |
|          |      |      |        |            |             |

÷ 100

1  4  2 . 7  ÷ 100 = ☐

(c)

| Hundreds | Tens | Ones | Tenths | Hundredths | Thousandths |
|---|---|---|---|---|---|
| 4 | 1 | 0 | | | |
| | | | | | |

÷ 1,000

4  1  0 . ÷ 1,000 = [ ]

(d)

| Hundreds | Tens | Ones | Tenths | Hundredths | Thousandths |
|---|---|---|---|---|---|
| | 2 | 5 | | | |
| | | | | | |

÷ 1,000

2  5 . ÷ 1,000 = [ ]

## Practice

**3** (a)  $0.1 \div 10 =$ [ ]     (b)  $0.01 \div 10 =$ [ ]

(c)  $16.59 \div 10 =$ [ ]     (d)  $32 \div 10 =$ [ ]

**4** (a)  $10 \div 100 =$ [ ]     (b)  $0.1 \div 100 =$ [ ]

(c)  $30.9 \div 100 =$ [ ]     (d)  $2,400.3 \div 100 =$ [ ]

**5** (a) $100 \div 1{,}000 = $ ☐

(b) $10 \div 1{,}000 = $ ☐

(c) $146 \div 1{,}000 = $ ☐

(d) $2{,}981 \div 1{,}000 = $ ☐

**6** (a) $18 \div 1{,}000 = $ ☐

(b) $278.1 \div 10 = $ ☐

(c) $41.3 \div 100 = $ ☐

(d) $2{,}003.1 \div 100 = $ ☐

(e) $89.89 \div 10 = $ ☐

(f) $16{,}004 \div 1{,}000 = $ ☐

**7** (a) $82.7 \div$ ☐ $= 8.27$

(b) $902 \div$ ☐ $= 0.902$

(c) ☐ $\div 100 = 0.034$

(d) $123.82 \div$ ☐ $= 12.382$

(e) ☐ $\div 10 = 70.18$

(f) $1{,}401 \div$ ☐ $= 1.401$

## Challenge

**8** (a) $0.3 \div 1{,}000 = $ ☐

(b) $0.13 \div 100 = $ ☐

(c) $0.08 \div$ ☐ $= 0.0008$

(d) $54.321 \div$ ☐ $= 5.4321$

## Basics

**1** (a) Express 8.7 cm in millimeters.

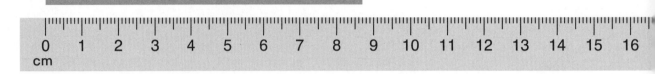

1 cm = 10 mm

8.7 cm = 8.7 × 10 mm = [        ] mm

(b) Express 75 mm in centimeters.

1 mm = 1 ÷ 10 cm

75 mm = 75 ÷ 10 cm = [        ] cm

**2** (a) Express 4.8 m in centimeters.

1 m = [        ] cm

4.8 m = 4.8 × [        ] cm = [        ] cm

(b) Express 14.7 cm in meters.

1 cm = 1 ÷ [        ] m

14.7 cm = 14.7 ÷ [        ] m = [        ] m

**3** (a) Express 6.89 km in meters.

1 km = ☐ m

6.89 km = 6.89 × ☐ m = ☐ m

(b) Express 12 m in kilometers.

1 m = 1 ÷ ☐ km

12 m = 12 ÷ ☐ km = ☐ km

**4** (a) Express 3.091 L in liters and milliliters.

0.091 L = 0.091 × ☐ mL = ☐ mL

3.091 L = ☐ L ☐ mL

(b) Express 5.89 L in milliliters.

5.89 L = 5.89 × ☐ mL = ☐ mL

**5** Express 2 kg 40 g in kilograms.

40 g = 40 ÷ ☐ kg = ☐ kg

2 kg 40 g = 2 kg + ☐ kg = ☐ kg

## Practice

**6** Find the equivalent measures in whole numbers or decimals.

(a) 0.5 m = ☐ cm

(b) 0.592 km = ☐ m

(c) 4.7 L = ☐ mL

(d) 0.03 kg = ☐ g

(e) 6.52 cm = ☐ mm

(f) 420 m = ☐ km

(g) 95 g = ☐ kg

(h) 362 mm = ☐ cm

(i) 1,842 mL = ☐ L

(j) 4,000 cm = ☐ m

**7** Find the equivalent measures.

(a) 3.2 kg = [ ] kg [ ] g

(b) 8.7 m = [ ] m [ ] cm

(c) 20.92 L = [ ] L [ ] mL

(d) 14 L 200 mL = [ ] mL

(e) 3 cm 7 mm = [ ] mm

(f) 10 km 80 m = [ ] m

**8** An exercise ball weighs 3.5 kg. How much does it weigh in grams?

**9** A piece of wire is 149.7 cm long. How long is it in meters?

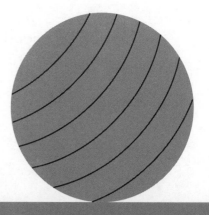

## Basics

**1** (a)  $15 \times 3 =$ ▢

(b)  15 tenths $\times$ 3 = ▢ tenths = ▢

(c)  15 hundredths $\times$ 3 = ▢ hundredths = ▢

(d)  15 thousandths $\times$ 3 = ▢ thousandths = ▢

**2**  $0.15 \times 3{,}000 = 0.15 \times 3 \times 1{,}000$

= 15 hundredths $\times$ 3 $\times$ 1,000

= ▢ hundredths $\times$ 1,000

= ▢ $\times$ 1,000

= ▢

**3** (a)  $36 \div 2 =$ ▢

(b)  36 tenths $\div$ 2 = ▢ tenths = ▢

(c)  36 hundredths $\div$ 2 = ▢ hundredths = ▢

(d)  36 thousandths $\div$ 2 = ▢ thousandths = ▢

**4**   $3.6 \div 200 = 3.6 \div 2 \div 100$

$\qquad = 36 \text{ tenths} \div 2 \div 100$

$\qquad = \boxed{\phantom{xxxx}} \text{ tenths} \div 100$

$\qquad = \boxed{\phantom{xxxx}} \div 100$

$\qquad = \boxed{\phantom{xxxx}}$

**5**   $2.8 \times 400 = 2.8 \times 4 \times 100$

$\qquad = \boxed{\phantom{xxxx}} \times 100$

$\qquad = \boxed{\phantom{xxxx}}$

**6**   (a)   $0.4 \div 8 = 0.40 \div 8$

$\qquad = \boxed{\phantom{xxxx}}$

(b)   $0.4 \div 80 = 0.40 \div 8 \div 10$

$\qquad = \boxed{\phantom{xxxx}}$

**7**   $0.015 \times 8{,}000 = 0.015 \times 8 \times 1{,}000$

$\qquad = \boxed{\phantom{xxxx}} \times 1{,}000$

$\qquad = \boxed{\phantom{xxxx}}$

## Practice

**8** Find the values.

(a) $0.3 \times 30 =$ [ ]

(b) $0.06 \times 800 =$ [ ]

(c) $0.006 \times 700 =$ [ ]

(d) $1.2 \times 400 =$ [ ]

(e) $0.025 \times 500 =$ [ ]

(f) $0.12 \times 30 =$ [ ]

(g) $4.2 \div 60 =$ [ ]

(h) $8 \div 2,000 =$ [ ]

(i) $56 \div 800 =$ [ ]

(j) $9.6 \div 300 =$ [ ]

(k) $14.8 \div 200 =$ [ ]

(l) $0.6 \div 50 =$ [ ]

**9** A pencil costs $0.35. How much do 20 pencils cost?

**10** 50 erasers cost $4.50. How much does 1 eraser cost?

## Check

**1** Complete the equations.

(a) $24 \div 1{,}000 =$ ⬚

(b) $0.089 \times 10 =$ ⬚

(c) $41.323 \times 100 =$ ⬚

(d) $3.1 \div 100 =$ ⬚

(e) $89.89 \div 10 =$ ⬚

(f) $0.04 \times 1{,}000 =$ ⬚

(g) $10.59 \times$ ⬚ $= 10{,}590$

(h) $7.5 \div$ ⬚ $= 0.075$

(i) ⬚ $\div 1{,}000 = 0.069$

(j) ⬚ $\times 100 = 7.6$

**2** Find the equivalent measures.

(a) $6.09 \text{ m} =$ ⬚ cm

(b) $2{,}060 \text{ g} =$ ⬚ kg

(c) $720 \text{ mL} =$ ⬚ L

(d) $2.08 \text{ km} =$ ⬚ m

(e) $0.7 \text{ mm} =$ ⬚ cm

(f) $0.77 \text{ kg} =$ ⬚ g

(g) $4 \text{ L } 50 \text{ mL} =$ ⬚ L

(h) $20 \text{ m } 20 \text{ cm} =$ ⬚ m

**3** Complete the equations.

(a) $0.007 \times 90 = \boxed{\phantom{000}}$

(b) $4.8 \div 800 = \boxed{\phantom{000}}$

(c) $2.1 \div 70 = \boxed{\phantom{000}}$

(d) $0.03 \times 6{,}000 = \boxed{\phantom{000}}$

(e) $2.08 \times 3{,}000 = \boxed{\phantom{000}}$

(f) $7.2 \div 600 = \boxed{\phantom{000}}$

(g) $155 \div 5{,}000 = \boxed{\phantom{000}}$

(h) $0.12 \times 80 = \boxed{\phantom{000}}$

(i) $\boxed{\phantom{000}} \times 600 = 3.6$

(j) $\boxed{\phantom{000}} \div 500 = 0.006$

**4** Complete the equations.

(a) $0.26 \times 10 = \boxed{\phantom{000}} \div 100$

(b) $7{,}200 \div 6{,}000 = \boxed{\phantom{000}} \times 300$

**5** Paul earned $8,040 for 400 hours of work as a life guard. How much was he paid for 8 hours of work?

**6** The total weight of 500 identical books is 160 kg. How much does one book weigh in grams?

**7** 1 inch is equal to 2.54 centimeters. How many centimeters are in 20 inches?

**8** 200 identical sheets of glass are 48 cm thick.

(a) How thick is 1 sheet of glass in centimeters?

(b) How thick is 1 sheet of glass in millimeters?

**9** 1 can contains 0.342 L of juice.

(a) How many liters of juice are in 200 of these cans?

(b) How many milliliters of juice are in 200 cans?

## Challenge

**10** Write × or ÷ in each ◯.

(a) 5.68 ◯ 700 = 3,976

(b) 8.28 ◯ 120 = 0.069

**11** At a supermarket, prawns are sold at $2.58 for 100 g. How much do 3 kg of prawns cost?

**12** (a) What is the least whole number that can be multiplied by 0.02 to get a whole number product?

(b) What is the least whole number that can be multiplied by 0.025 to get a whole number product?

# Chapter 10 The Four Operations of Decimals

## Basics

**1** (a) Estimate the sum of 8.259 and 17.78.

8.259 + 17.78 ≈ 8 + 18 = ▭

(b) Find the sum of 8.259 and 17.78.

```
    1 7 . 7 8
  +   8 . 2 5 9
  _____
```

**2** (a) Estimate the sum of 0.361 and 13.7.

0.361 + 13.7 ≈ 0.4 + 14 = ▭

(b) Find the sum of 0.361 and 13.7.

```
    1 3 . 7
  +   0 . 3 6 1
  _____
```

**3** (a) Estimate the sum of 0.14, 7.349, and 62.7.

0.14 + 7.349 + 62.7 ≈ 0 + 7 + 63 = ▭

(b) Find the sum of 0.14, 7.349, and 62.7.

```
      0 . 1 4
      7 . 3 4 9
  + 6 2 . 7
  _____
```

## Practice

**4** Write > or < in each ◯. Use estimation.

(a)  0.945 + 1.9 ◯ 2.34 + 1.706

(b)  0.062 + 0.004 ◯ 0.05 + 0.29

(c)  14.95 + 8.982 ◯ 19.2 + 0.969

**5** Add.

(a)  9.356 + 5.26

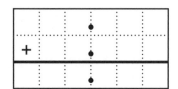

(b)  183.3 + 16.828

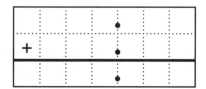

(c)  0.802 + 3.394

(d)  55.4 + 36.824

(e)  82 + 9.06 + 0.039

(f)  200.7 + 19.46 + 7.041

## Basics

**1** (a) Estimate the value of 8.259 − 7.78.

$$8.259 - 7.78 \approx 8.3 - 8 = \boxed{\phantom{000}}$$

(b) Subtract 7.78 from 8.259.

```
    8.2 5 9
 -  7.7 8
 _____
```

**2** (a) Estimate the value of 42.56 − 13.621.

$$42.56 - 13.621 \approx 40 - 10 = \boxed{\phantom{000}}$$

(b) Subtract 13.621 from 42.56.

```
   4 2.5 6 0
 - 1 3.6 2 1
 _____
```

**3** (a) Estimate the difference between 19.459 and 142.3.

$$142.3 - 19.459 \approx \boxed{\phantom{000}}$$

(b) Find the difference between 19.459 and 142.3.

```
   1 4 2.3
 -   1 9.4 5 9
 _____
```

## Practice

**4** Write > or < in each ◯. Use estimation.

(a)  2.9 – 0.945 ◯ 32 – 23.6

(b)  0.062 – 0.004 ◯ 0.34 – 0.09

(c)  11.8 – 8.982 ◯ 0.87 + 0.012

**5** Subtract.

(a)  9.356 – 5.26

(b)  186.3 – 16.828

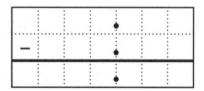

(c)  5.802 – 3.39

(d)  12.307 – 7.7

(e)  50 – 36.824

(f)  10.4 – 9.461

**6** In a laboratory, 0.069 g of Compound A is mixed with 0.348 g of Compound B. Compound C is added to bring the total mixture to 1 g. How many grams of Compound C is added?

## Challenge

**7** Find the values. Express the answers as decimals.

(a) $6\frac{9}{40} - \frac{7}{8} + 8.23$

(b) $10\frac{3}{4} + 3\frac{1}{2} - (0.08 + \frac{93}{200})$

## Basics

**1** (a)

× 0.1 → × 0.1 → × 0.1 →

324 ☐ ☐ ☐

(b) $324 × 0.1 = 324 × \frac{1}{10} = \boxed{\dfrac{\phantom{0}}{10}} = \boxed{\phantom{00000}}$

(c) $32.4 × 0.1 = \frac{324}{10} × \frac{1}{10} = \boxed{\dfrac{\phantom{0}}{100}} = \boxed{\phantom{00000}}$

(d) $324 × 0.01 = 324 × \frac{1}{100} = \boxed{\dfrac{\phantom{0}}{100}} = \boxed{\phantom{00000}}$

(e) $32.4 × 0.01 = \frac{324}{10} × \frac{1}{100} = \boxed{\dfrac{\phantom{0}}{1{,}000}} = \boxed{\phantom{00000}}$

**2** Complete the charts and fill in the blanks.

(a)

| Hundreds | Tens | Ones | Tenths | Hundredths | Thousandths |
|---|---|---|---|---|---|
|  |  | 8 | 3 | 2 |  |
|  |  |  |  |  |  |

× 0.1

$8 . 3 \ 2 \ × 0.1 = \boxed{\phantom{00000}}$

(b)

| Hundreds | Tens | Ones | Tenths | Hundredths | Thousandths |
|----------|------|------|--------|------------|-------------|
| 1 | 4 | 2 . | 7 | | |
| | | . | | | |

×0.01

1 4 2 . 7  × 0.01 = ⬚

## Practice

**3** (a) 500 × 0.1 = ⬚  (b) 500 × 0.01 = ⬚

(c) 50 × 0.1 = ⬚  (d) 50 × 0.01 = ⬚

(e) 5 × 0.1 = ⬚  (f) 5 × 0.01 = ⬚

(g) 0.5 × 0.1 = ⬚  (h) 0.5 × 0.01 = ⬚

**4** (a) 3.2 × 0.1 = ⬚  (b) 3.2 × 0.01 = ⬚

(c) 45 × 0.1 = ⬚  (d) 45 × 0.01 = ⬚

(e) 800.8 × 0.1 = ⬚  (f) 800.8 × 0.01 = ⬚

**5** (a) $23 \times 0.01 = \boxed{\phantom{xxx}}$      (b) $3.54 \times 0.1 = \boxed{\phantom{xxx}}$

(c) $0.07 \times 0.1 = \boxed{\phantom{xxx}}$      (d) $430 \times 0.01 = \boxed{\phantom{xxx}}$

(e) $46.02 \times 0.1 = \boxed{\phantom{xxx}}$      (f) $5{,}560 \times 0.01 = \boxed{\phantom{xxx}}$

**6** (a) $3.73 \times \boxed{\phantom{xxx}} = 0.373$      (b) $1.2 \times \boxed{\phantom{xxx}} = 0.012$

(c) $\boxed{\phantom{xxx}} \times 0.01 = 65$      (d) $\boxed{\phantom{xxx}} \times 0.1 = 8.92$

**7** 4 L of sand weigh 1 kg 92 g. How many grams does 0.1 L of this sand weigh?

## Challenge

**8** (a) $500 \times 0.001 = \boxed{\phantom{xxx}}$      (b) $50 \times 0.001 = \boxed{\phantom{xxx}}$

(c) $0.5 \times 0.001 = \boxed{\phantom{xxx}}$      (d) $0.05 \times 0.01 = \boxed{\phantom{xxx}}$

## Basics

**1** (a) $45 \times 0.8 = 45 \times 8 \times 0.1 = \boxed{\phantom{xxx}} \times 0.1 = \boxed{\phantom{xxx}}$

(b) $4.5 \times 0.8 = 45 \times 8 \times 0.1 \times 0.1 = \boxed{\phantom{xxx}}$

(c) $4.5 \times 0.08 = 45 \times 8 \times 0.1 \times 0.01 = \boxed{\phantom{xxx}}$

(d) $0.45 \times 0.8 = 45 \times 8 \times 0.01 \times 0.1 = \boxed{\phantom{xxx}}$

**2** (a) Estimate the value of $503 \times 55$.

$503 \times 55 \approx 500 \times 60 = \boxed{\phantom{xxx}}$

(b) Find the value of $503 \times 55$.

$503 \times 55 = \boxed{\phantom{xxx}}$

$$\begin{array}{r} 5\ \ 0\ \ 3 \\ \times \quad\ 5\ \ 5 \\ \hline \end{array}$$

(c) Estimate the value of $50.3 \times 0.55$.

$50.3 \times 0.55 \approx 50 \times 0.6 = \boxed{\phantom{xxx}}$

(d) Find the value of $50.3 \times 0.55$.

$50.3 \times 0.55 = \boxed{\phantom{xxx}}$

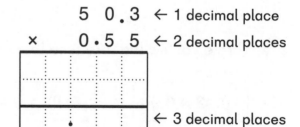

$5\ 0.3$ ← 1 decimal place
$\times \quad 0.5\ 5$ ← 2 decimal places

← 3 decimal places

**3** (a) Estimate the value of $42.5 \times 0.6$.

$$42.5 \times 0.6 \approx 40 \times 0.6 = \boxed{\phantom{0000}}$$

(b) Find the value of $42.5 \times 0.6$

$$
\begin{array}{r}
4\ 2.5 \leftarrow \text{1 decimal place} \\
\times \quad\quad 0.6 \leftarrow \text{1 decimal place} \\
\hline
\boxed{\ \ |\ \ |\,\cdot\,|\ \ } \leftarrow \text{2 decimal places}
\end{array}
$$

## Practice

**4** Estimate the values.

(a) $482 \times 7 \approx 500 \times 7 = \boxed{\phantom{0000}}$

(b) $482 \times 0.7 \approx 500 \times 0.7 = \boxed{\phantom{0000}}$

(c) $48.2 \times 0.7 \approx 50 \times 0.7 = \boxed{\phantom{0000}}$

(d) $4.82 \times 0.7 \approx 5 \times 0.7 = \boxed{\phantom{0000}}$

(e) $48.2 \times 0.07 \approx 50 \times 0.07 = \boxed{\phantom{0000}}$

**5** Circle values that are less than 1. Use estimation.

| $0.42 \times 0.9$ | $3.92 \times 0.4$ | $8.9 \times 0.07$ | $1.8 \times 0.32$ |

**6** Use the fact that 987 × 78 = 76,986 to find the following values.

(a) 987 × 0.78 = ⬚

(b) 98.7 × 7.8 = ⬚

(c) 9.87 × 7.8 = ⬚

(d) 98.7 × 0.78 = ⬚

**7** Find the values. Remember to estimate first.

(a) 0.23 × 0.8

(b) 9.2 × 1.6

(c) 4.07 × 6.2

(d) 120.5 × 0.42

## Check

**1** Is the sum of 0.14, 0.719, and 5.4 closer to 6 or 7? Use estimation.

**2** Find the values.

(a) 6.37 + 0.268

(b) 0.802 − 0.072

(c) 55.55 − 0.777

(d) 23.4 + 9.427 + 0.8

**3** (a) 56.2 × 0.1 = ☐

(b) 8.9 × 0.01 = ☐

(c) 50.8 × 0.01 = ☐

(d) 189.2 × 0.1 = ☐

(e) 0.5 × 0.02 = ☐

(f) 0.07 × 0.4 = ☐

(g) 40.9 × 0.4 = ☐

(h) 2.5 × 0.08 = ☐

**4** Draw a line to connect each product with its location on the number line. Use estimation.

40.1 × 0.09          0.56 × 0.6          0.03 × 23.8          0.06 × 87.3

```
0    1    2    3    4    5    6    7    8
```

**5** Write > or < in each ◯.

(a)  0.04 × 0.95 ◯ 0.04

(b)  0.2 ◯ 2.91 × 0.04

(c)  3.8 × 0.62 ◯ 6.98 × 0.5

**6** Find the values.

(a)  38.24 × 0.3                    (b)  0.04 × 62.1

(c)  198 × 0.15                    (d)  6.07 × (6.27 + 0.83)

**7** Janice has 3.5 kg of flour. She used 325 g of it to make cookies and 2.45 kg of it to make bread. How many kilograms of flour does she have left?

**8** One inch is equal to 2.54 cm. How many centimeters are in 4.5 inches?

**9** James earns $23.80 an hour at his job. He gets paid 1.5 times as much for each hour a week that he works over 40 hours. Last week he worked 47 hours. What was his pay last week?

## Challenge

**10** Find the values.

(a) 0.025 × 0.04 × 2,000

(b) 200 × 0.02 × 0.002 × 2

(c) 0.0125 × 800 × 4,000 × 0.002

**11** Find the missing digits. No numbers can have trailing zeros (in 3.20 and 4.00, the 0's are called trailing zeros.)

(a) 2 0 . ☐ × 0 . ☐ = 6 . ☐ 2

(b) 0.2 × ☐ . ☐ = ☐ . 1

(c) ☐ . 4 × ☐ . ☐ = 0.0 0 2

## Basics

**1** (a) 4.8 ÷ 8 = 48 tenths ÷ 8 = 6 tenths = ▢

(b) 0.72 ÷ 9 = 72 hundredths ÷ 9 = ▢ hundredths = ▢

(c) 0.03 ÷ 6 = 30 thousandths ÷ 6 = ▢ thousandths = ▢

**2** (a) Complete the following estimations for 9.3 ÷ 4.

8 ÷ 4 = ▢          12 ÷ 4 = ▢

The quotient will be between _____ and _____.

(b) Divide 9.3 by 4.

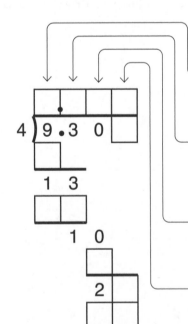

9 ones ÷ 4 is _____ ones with 1 one left over.

13 tenths ÷ 4 is _____ tenths with 1 tenth left over.

10 hundredths ÷ 4 is _____ hundredths with 2 hundredths left over.

20 thousandths ÷ 4 is _____ thousandths.

(c) Check: 2.325 × 4 = ▢

**3** (a) Complete the following estimation for 0.635 ÷ 5.

0.60 ÷ 5 = ☐

(b) Divide 0.635 by 5.

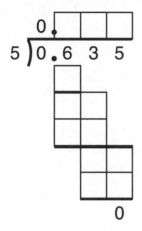

**4** (a) Complete the following estimations for 92.85 ÷ 15.

100 ÷ 10 = ☐          90 ÷ 15 = ☐

(b) Divide 92.85 by 15.

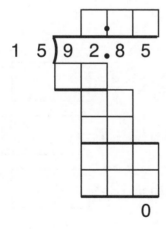

## Practice

**5** Which of the following has a quotient between 0.1 and 1? Use estimation.

| 8.35 ÷ 9 | | 6.72 ÷ 4 | | 5.81 ÷ 7 | | 0.62 ÷ 5 |

**6** Estimate the values.

(a)  $1{,}789 \div 32 \approx 1{,}800 \div 30 =$ ☐

(b)  $178.9 \div 32 \approx 180 \div 30 =$ ☐

(c)  $17.89 \div 32 \approx 18 \div 30 =$ ☐

(d)  $1.789 \div 32 \approx 1.8 \div 30 =$ ☐

**7** Which of the following has a quotient between 0.1 and 1?

| 135.9 ÷ 89 | | 6.72 ÷ 41 | | 16.14 ÷ 19 | | 0.05 ÷ 45 |

**8** (a)  $4.2 \div 7 =$ ☐  (b)  $0.064 \div 8 =$ ☐

(c)  $0.12 \div 20 =$ ☐  (d)  $12.012 \div 4 =$ ☐

(e)  $0.4 \div 50 =$ ☐  (f)  $0.06 \div 12 =$ ☐

**9** Divide.

(a) $5.238 \div 3$

(b) $19.84 \div 62$

(c) $37.08 \div 18$

(d) $484.6 \div 25$

**10** In a laboratory, 4.56 g of residue is divided equally into 5 test tubes. How many grams of residue is in each test tube?

## Basics

**1** Express $\frac{9}{11}$ as a decimal correct to the second decimal place.

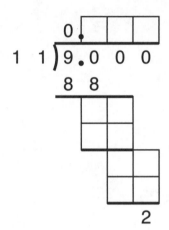

$\frac{9}{11}$ is _____, correct to the second decimal place.

**2** Express $8\frac{63}{64}$ as a decimal correct to the second decimal place.

$8\frac{63}{64} = 8 + \frac{63}{64}$

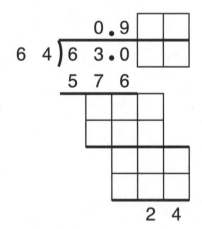

$8\frac{63}{64} \approx$ ☐

**3** (a) Complete the following estimations for 17.51 ÷ 29.

$15 \div 30 =$ ☐          $18 \div 30 =$ ☐

(b) Find the value of 17.51 ÷ 29, correct to the second decimal place.

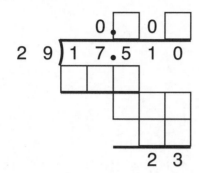

17.51 ÷ 29 is _____, correct to the second decimal place.

## Practice

**4** Express each fraction or mixed number as a decimal correct to the second decimal place.

(a) $\frac{2}{3}$                      (b) $1\frac{7}{9}$

(c) $\frac{9}{14}$                     (d) $2\frac{11}{16}$

**5** Divide. Express the quotients correct to the second decimal place.

(a)  $45.2 \div 6$

(b)  $8.11 \div 7$

(c)  $35.77 \div 21$

(d)  $406.7 \div 13$

## Challenge

**6** Continue to divide $\frac{9}{11}$ past the thousandths place. Which digits repeat?

**7** Continue to divide $\frac{6}{55}$ past the thousandths place. Which digits repeat?

## Exercise 8

### Basics

**1**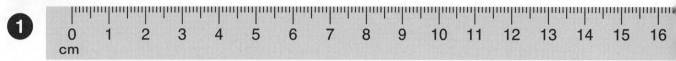

(a) 1 mm = $\frac{1}{10}$ cm = 0.1 cm

There are _____ mm in 1 cm.

There are _____ 0.1 cm in 1 cm.

$1 \div 0.1 = 1 \div \frac{1}{10} = 1 \times \boxed{\phantom{xxx}} = \boxed{\phantom{xxx}}$

(b) $5 \div 0.1 = 5 \div \frac{1}{10} = 5 \times \boxed{\phantom{xxx}} = \boxed{\phantom{xxx}}$

(c) $50 \div 0.1 = 50 \div \frac{1}{10} = 50 \times \boxed{\phantom{xxx}} = \boxed{\phantom{xxx}}$

(d) $500 \div 0.1 = 500 \div \frac{1}{10} = 500 \times \boxed{\phantom{xxx}} = \boxed{\phantom{xxx}}$

**2**

| 0 | 0.5 | 1 |
|---|-----|---|

(a) $1 \div 0.01 = 1 \div \frac{1}{100} = 1 \times \boxed{\phantom{xxx}} = \boxed{\phantom{xxx}}$

(b) $5 \div 0.01 = 5 \div \frac{1}{100} = 5 \times \boxed{\phantom{xxx}} = \boxed{\phantom{xxx}}$

(c) $50 \div 0.01 = 50 \div \frac{1}{100} = 50 \times \boxed{\phantom{xxx}} = \boxed{\phantom{xxx}}$

(d) $500 \div 0.01 = 500 \div \frac{1}{100} = 500 \times \boxed{\phantom{xxx}} = \boxed{\phantom{xxx}}$

## Practice

**3** (a) $42 \div 0.1 = \boxed{\phantom{xxx}}$        (b) $42 \div 0.01 = \boxed{\phantom{xxx}}$

(c) $104 \div 0.1 = \boxed{\phantom{xxx}}$        (d) $104 \div 0.01 = \boxed{\phantom{xxx}}$

(e) $9 \div 0.01 = \boxed{\phantom{xxx}}$        (f) $100 \div 0.1 = \boxed{\phantom{xxx}}$

(g) $72 \div 0.1 = \boxed{\phantom{xxx}}$        (h) $16 \div 0.01 = \boxed{\phantom{xxx}}$

(i) $3 \div 0.01 = \boxed{\phantom{xxx}}$        (j) $40 \div 0.01 = \boxed{\phantom{xxx}}$

(k) $400 \div 0.1 = \boxed{\phantom{xxx}}$        (l) $2{,}400 \div 0.1 = \boxed{\phantom{xxx}}$

**4** A laboratory technician has 4 g of substrate. She needs to put 0.1 g into each test tube. How many test tubes does she need?

## Challenge

**5** (a) $1 \div 0.001 = \boxed{\phantom{xxx}}$        (b) $5 \div 0.001 = \boxed{\phantom{xxx}}$

(c) $50 \div 0.001 = \boxed{\phantom{xxx}}$        (d) $500 \div 0.01 = \boxed{\phantom{xxx}}$

## Basics

**1** (a) Divide 60 by 4.

$$60 \div 4 = \boxed{\phantom{xxxx}}$$

(b) Divide 6 by 0.4.

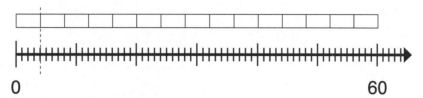

$$6 \div 0.4 = 6 \div \frac{4}{10} = 6 \times \frac{10}{4} = \boxed{\phantom{xxxx}}$$

(c) $6 \div 0.4 = 60 \div 4 = \boxed{\phantom{xxxx}}$

**2** (a) $24 \div 1.2 = 24 \div \frac{12}{10} = 24 \times \frac{10}{12} = \boxed{\phantom{xxxx}}$

(b) $2\ 4\ .\ \ \div\ 1\ .\ 2\ \ = \boxed{\phantom{xxxx}} \div 12 = \boxed{\phantom{xxxx}}$

(c) $24 \div 0.12 = 24 \div \frac{12}{100} = 24 \times \boxed{\dfrac{\phantom{x}}{12}} = \boxed{\phantom{xxxx}}$

(d) $2\ 4\ .\ \ \div\ 0\ .\ 1\ 2\ \ = \boxed{\phantom{xxxx}} \div 12 = \boxed{\phantom{xxxx}}$

**3** Divide 73 by 0.4.

　　　→　　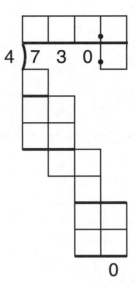

73 ÷ 0.4 = ⬚

**4** Estimate the quotient of 73 ÷ 3.1. Then find the quotient correct to the second decimal place.

7 3. ÷ 3.1 = 730 ÷ 31 ≈ 600 ÷ 30 = ⬚

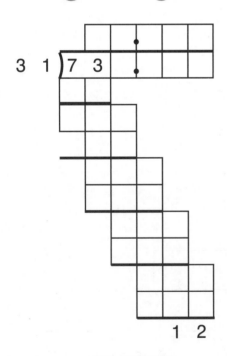

73 ÷ 3.1 ≈ ⬚

## Practice

**5** (a) $18 \div 0.6 =$ [ ]      (b) $6 \div 0.05 =$ [ ]

     (c) $75 \div 2.5 =$ [ ]      (d) $44 \div 0.22 =$ [ ]

**6** Divide. Express quotients with 3 or more decimal places correct to the second decimal place.

     (a) $760 \div 0.25$                 (b) $49 \div 0.08$

     (c) $78 \div 0.9$                 (d) $430 \div 4.5$

**7** 130 g of tea is put into tea bags. Each bag gets 2.5 g of tea. How many bags are needed?

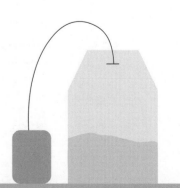

## Check

**1**  (a) 6.4 ÷ 8 = [ ]  (b) 0.24 ÷ 4 = [ ]

(c) 0.3 × 0.4 ÷ 6 = [ ]  (d) 0.48 ÷ 4 × 5 = [ ]

(e) 89 ÷ 0.1 = [ ]  (f) 3 ÷ 0.01 = [ ]

(g) 1,000 ÷ 0.1 = [ ]  (h) 12 ÷ 0.01 = [ ]

(i) 9 ÷ 0.1 × 0.1 = [ ]  (j) 9 ÷ (0.1 × 0.1) = [ ]

(k) 4 ÷ 0.8 = [ ]  (l) 81 ÷ 0.09 = [ ]

(m) 30 × 0.4 ÷ 0.02 = [ ]  (n) 30 ÷ 0.4 × 0.02 = [ ]

**2** Circle the values that are equal.

(a) | 32 ÷ 0.6 | | 320 ÷ 0.6 | | 32 ÷ 60 | | 320 ÷ 6 |

(b) | 4.8 ÷ 8 | | 48 ÷ 0.08 | | 480 ÷ 8 | | 480 ÷ 0.8 |

**3** Write > or < in each ◯. Use estimation.

(a)  9.8 ÷ 72 ◯ 12.62 ÷ 8

(b)  26 ÷ 0.08 ◯ 269 ÷ 0.39

(c)  1,058 ÷ 9.9 ◯ 98 ÷ 0.5

**4** Find the values. Express quotients with 3 or more decimal places correct to the second decimal place.

(a)  89.5 ÷ 6                    (b)  9 ÷ 0.08

(c)  8 ÷ 4.5                     (d)  32 ÷ 0.14

(e)  7 ÷ 0.05 × 0.6              (f)  4.576 + 8.3 ÷ 25

**5** 15.8 L of a solvent is poured equally into 8 beakers. How many liters are in each beaker?

**6** How many 3.8 m pieces can be cut from 100 m of rope?

**7** Sonia bought 1.5 lb of morel mushrooms for $72. What does 1 pound of morel mushrooms cost?

# Chapter 11 Geometry

## Basics

**1** Write 0°, 90°, 180°, or 360° in each blank to complete the table.

| | | |
|---|---|---|
| | acute angle | between _____ and _____ |
| | right angle | equal to _____ |
| | obtuse angle | between _____ and _____ |
| | straight angle | equal to _____ |
| | reflex angle | between _____ and _____ |
| | full turn | equal to _____ |

**2**

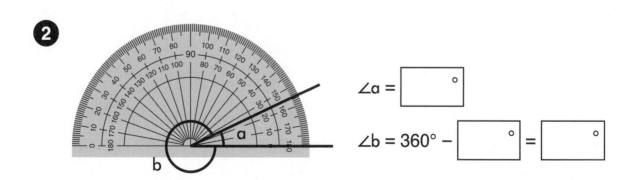

∠a = [＿＿] °

∠b = 360° − [＿＿] ° = [＿＿] °

**3**

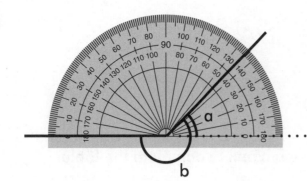

$\angle a = \boxed{\phantom{xxx}}^{\circ}$

$\angle b = 180^{\circ} + \boxed{\phantom{xxx}}^{\circ} = \boxed{\phantom{xxx}}^{\circ}$

**4** Estimate the measure of the reflex angle. Then use a protractor to find the measure.

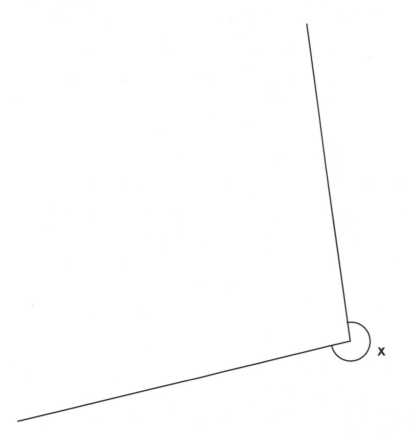

Estimate: A little less than 3 right angles, so a little less than _____.

$\angle x = \boxed{\phantom{xxx}}^{\circ}$

## Practice

**5** Estimate the size of each reflex angle. Then measure each angle with a protractor.

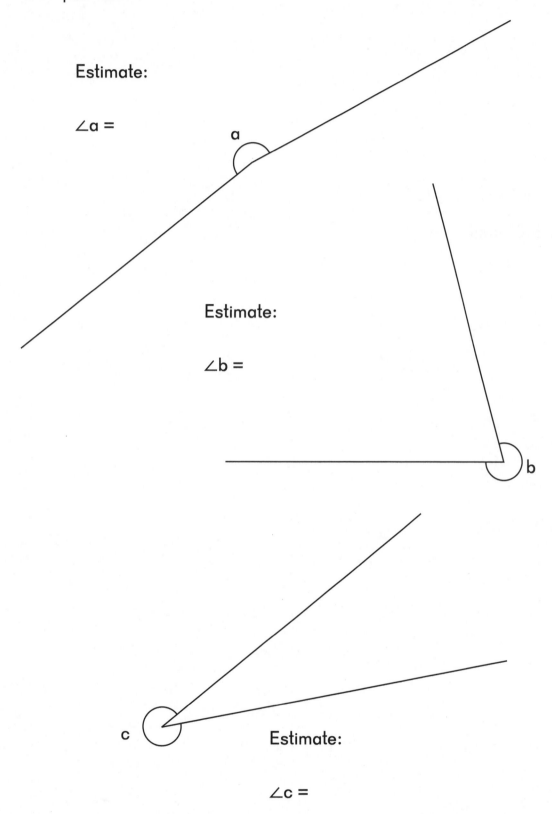

Estimate:

∠a =

Estimate:

∠b =

Estimate:

∠c =

**6** Draw a 135° angle.

**7** Draw a 200° angle.

**8** Draw a 317° angle.

## Exercise 2

### Basics

**1** The figure below shows two straight lines that intersect. $\angle a = 45°$.

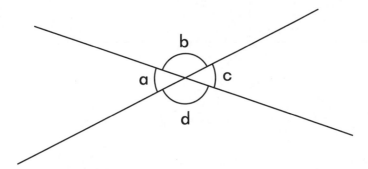

(a) $\angle a$ and $\angle b$ are adjacent angles. Name three other pairs of adjacent angles.

(b) The sum of adjacent angles on a line is _____.

(c) $\angle b = 180° - 45° = \boxed{\phantom{00}}°$

$\angle c = 180° - \boxed{\phantom{00}}° = \boxed{\phantom{00}}°$

$\angle d = 180° - \boxed{\phantom{00}}° = \boxed{\phantom{00}}°$

(d) $\angle a = \angle \boxed{\phantom{0}}$

$\angle b = \angle \boxed{\phantom{0}}$

(e) $\angle a$ and $\angle c$ are vertical angles. Name another pair of vertical angles.

(f) $\angle a + \angle b + \angle c + \angle d = \boxed{\phantom{00}}°$

**2** MN and PQ are straight lines that intersect at O. ∠AON is a right angle.

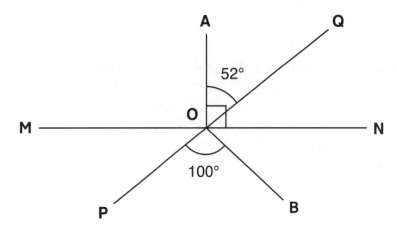

(a) ∠QON = [　　]° − 52° = [　　]°

(b) ∠MOP = [　　]°

(c) ∠NOB = 180° − 100° − [　　]° = [　　]°

## Practice

**3** In the following figures, MN is a straight line. Find the measure of each unknown marked angle.

(a)

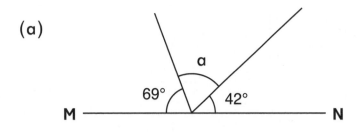

(b)

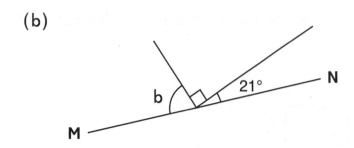

**4** Find the measure of each unknown marked angle.

(a)

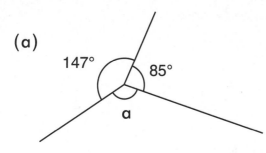

147°   85°

a

(b)

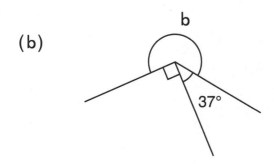

b

37°

**5** In the following figures, MN and PQ are straight lines. Find the measure of each unknown marked angle.

(a)

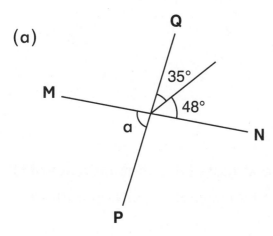

Q

35°

M

48°

a

N

P

(b)

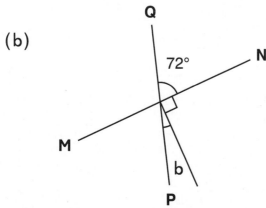

Q

72°   N

M

b

P

**6** In the following figures, MN and PQ are straight lines that intersect at O. Find the measure of each unknown marked angle.

(a)

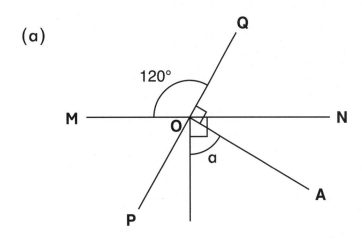

(b)

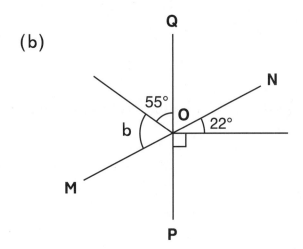

## Challenge

**7** In the following figure, MN and PQ are straight lines that intersect at O. ∠MOA is a right angle. ∠AOQ is twice as large as ∠QON. Find the measure of ∠x.

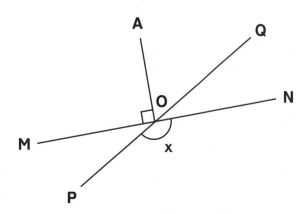

## Basics

| Shape | Name | Properties |
|---|---|---|
| | equilateral triangle | _____ equal sides<br><br>_____ equal angles |
| | isosceles triangle | _____ equal sides<br><br>_____ equal angles |
| | scalene triangle | _____ equal sides<br><br>_____ equal angles |
| | right triangle | has one angle that is _____° |
| | acute triangle | all angles are less than _____° |
| | obtuse triangle | has an angle greater than _____° |

# Practice

**2** (a) Match.

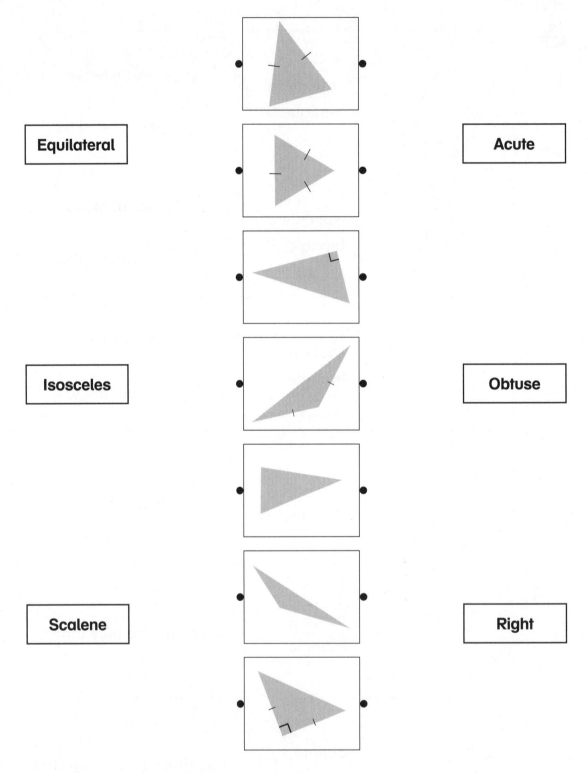

Equilateral

Acute

Isosceles

Obtuse

Scalene

Right

(b) Circle the equal angles of each triangle, if any.

**3** What is the measure of each unknown marked angle?

(a)

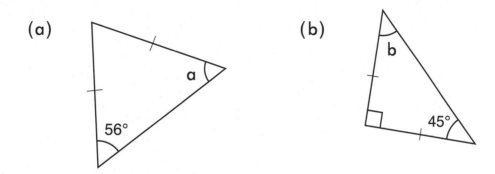

(b)

**4** In the following figure, AB = BC, AD is a straight line, and ∠BCD = 115°. What is the measure of ∠BAC?

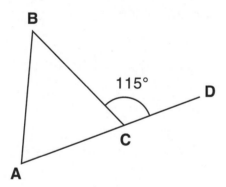

## Challenge

**5** In the following figure, AB = BC, AG and BF are straight lines, ∠BCG is four times as large as ∠BAC, and ∠BAC is twice as large as ∠DAB. Find the measure of ∠DAB.

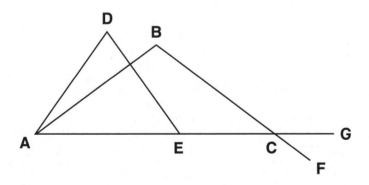

### Basics

**1**

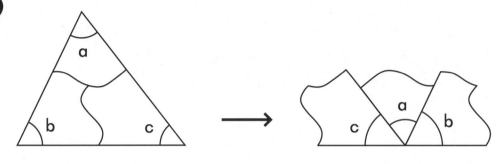

$\angle a + \angle b + \angle c = \boxed{\phantom{XXX}}^\circ$

**2** Find the measure of each unknown marked angle.

(a)

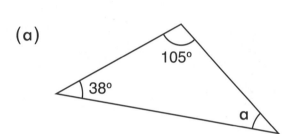

$\angle a = 180° − (38° + 105°) = \boxed{\phantom{XXX}}^\circ$

(b)

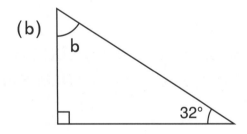

$\angle b = 90° − \boxed{\phantom{XX}}^\circ = \boxed{\phantom{XX}}^\circ$

(c)

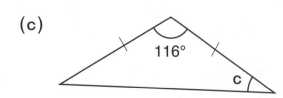

$\angle c = (180° − \boxed{\phantom{XX}}^\circ) ÷ 2 = \boxed{\phantom{XX}}^\circ$

**3** In the figure below, ABC is an equilateral triangle, DE = AE, and ∠CAD is half as large as ∠CAB. Find the measure of ∠a.

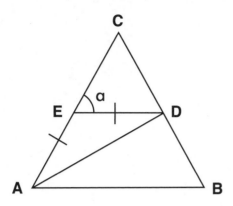

$∠CAB = \frac{1}{3} \times$ ☐° $= 60°$

$∠CAD = \frac{1}{2} \times 60° =$ ☐°

$∠AED = 180° - 2 \times$ ☐° $=$ ☐°

$∠a = 180° -$ ☐° $=$ ☐°

## Practice

**4** Find the measure of each unknown marked angle.

(a)

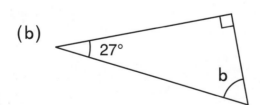

42°   a

23°

(b)

27°

b

(c)

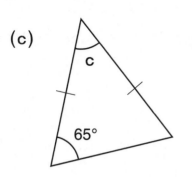

(d)

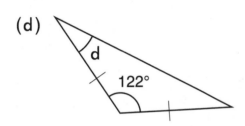

**5** In the following figures, MN and PQ are straight lines. Find the measure of each unknown marked angle.

(a)

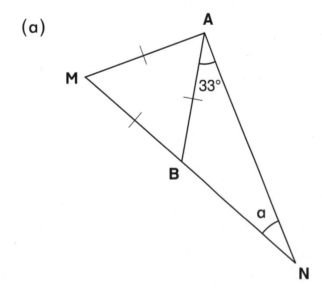

(b)

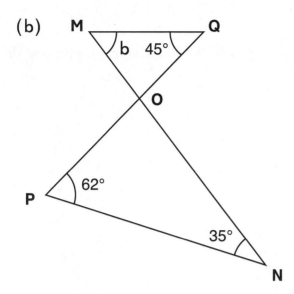

(c)

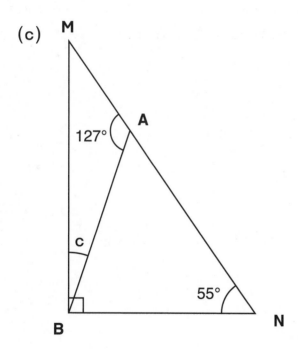

## Challenge

**6** A rectangular piece of paper is folded at two of its corners as shown. What is the measure of ∠p?

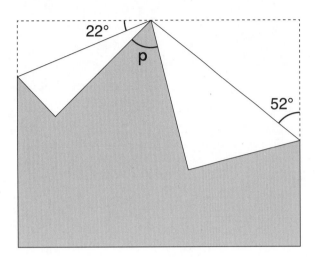

**7** In the figure below, MN, PQ, and RS are straight lines. What is the value of ∠a + ∠b + ∠c + ∠d + ∠e + ∠f? Hint: What is the value of ∠x + ∠y + ∠z?

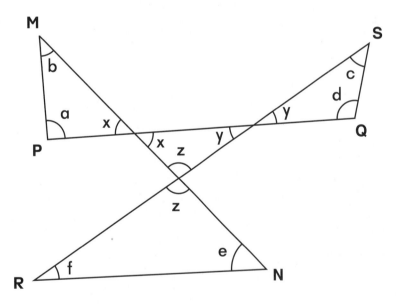

## Basics

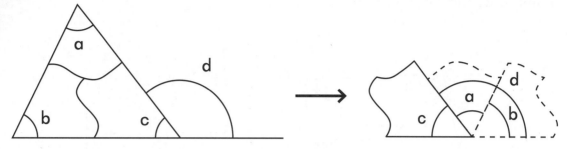

$\angle a + \angle b = \boxed{\phantom{00}}^{\circ} - \angle c$      $\angle d = \boxed{\phantom{00}}^{\circ} - \angle c$

$\angle a + \angle\boxed{\phantom{0}} = \angle d$

**2** Express each of the exterior angles $\angle x$, $\angle y$, and $\angle z$ as the sum of two internal angles of the triangle.

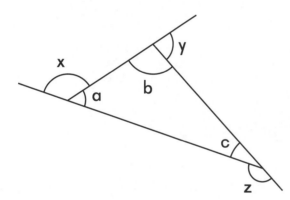

$\angle x = \angle\boxed{\phantom{0}} + \angle\boxed{\phantom{0}}$

$\angle y = \angle\boxed{\phantom{0}} + \angle\boxed{\phantom{0}}$

$\angle z = \angle\boxed{\phantom{0}} + \angle\boxed{\phantom{0}}$

**3** In the figure below, MN is a straight line. Find the measure of $\angle a$.

$\angle a = 105° + 38° = \boxed{\phantom{000}}^{\circ}$

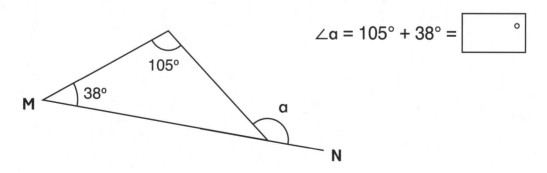

## Practice

**4** In the figure below, MN and PQ are straight lines. Complete the equations using only the marked angles.

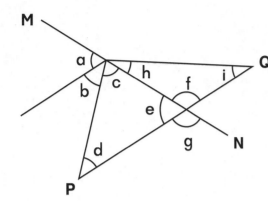

$\angle h + \angle i = \angle \boxed{\phantom{0}}$

$\angle d + \angle e = \angle a + \angle \boxed{\phantom{0}}$

**5** In the figures below, lines MN and MR are straight lines. Find the measure of each unknown marked angle.

(a)

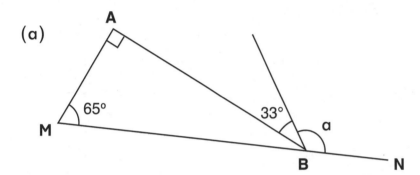

(b)

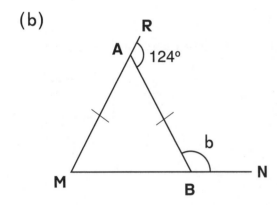

(c)

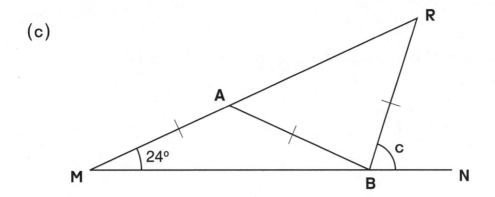

**6** ABC and ADE are isosceles triangles. Find the measures of ∠x and ∠y.

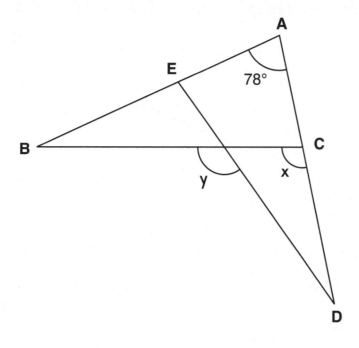

## Challenge

**7** What is the sum of the three exterior angles of a triangle?

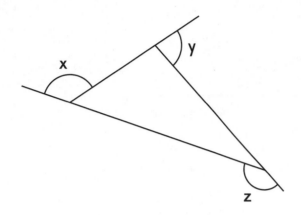

**8** The figure below shows two overlapping triangles, ABC and ADC. BE = EC.
Find the measure of ∠a.

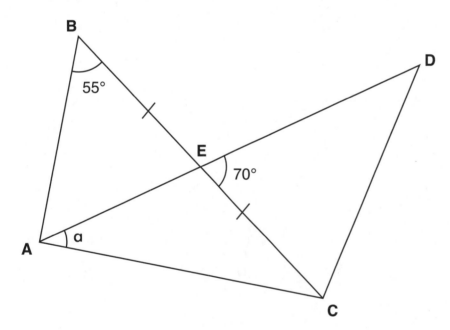

## Basics

**1** Fill in the blanks.

| | |
|---|---|
| | A quadrilateral is a closed figure with _____ straight sides. |
| | A trapezoid is a quadrilateral with at least _____ pair of _____ sides. |
| | A parallelogram is a trapezoid with _____ pairs of _____ sides. |
| | A rhombus is a parallelogram with _____ equal sides. |
| | A rectangle is a parallelogram with 4 _____ angles. |
| | A square is a rhombus that is also a _____. |

**2** True or false?

(a) All parallelograms are trapezoids. _____

(b) All trapezoids are parallelograms. _____

(c) A trapezoid can be a rhombus. _____

(d) All parallelograms have 2 equal sides. _____

# Practice

**3** Complete the table.

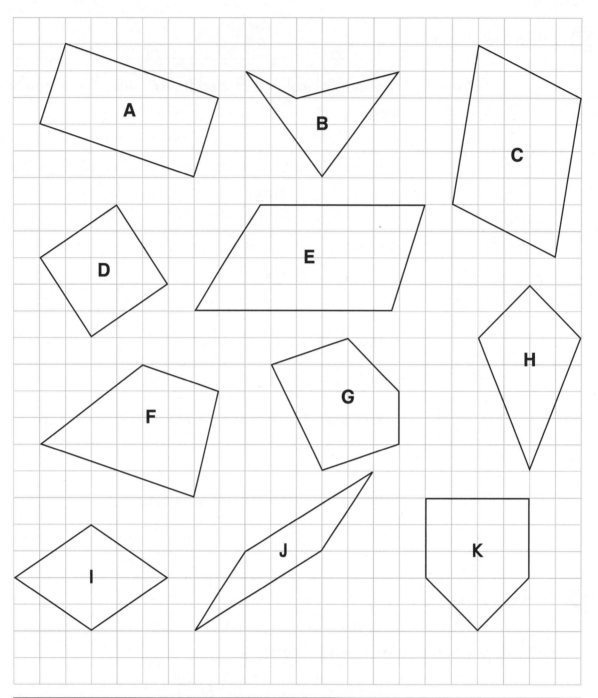

| Quadrilateral | Trapezoid | Parallelogram | Rhombus | Rectangle | Square |
|---|---|---|---|---|---|
| A, | | | | | |

**4** In naming shapes, the vertices are named in order around the shape. The square to the right can be named Square TEAM, EAMT, MAET, etc, but not MEAT.

Complete each drawing to draw the given shape.

(a) Square STEM

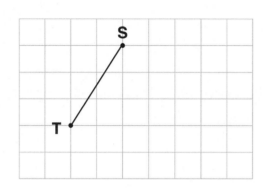

(b) Square LEAF

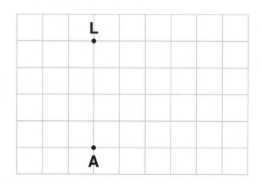

(c) Rectangle RECT

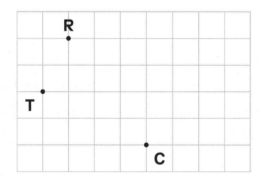

(d) Parallelogram EAST

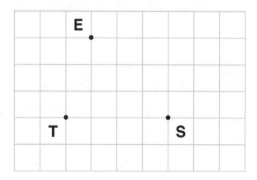

(e) Parallelogram WEST

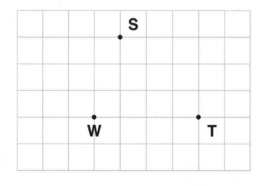

(f) Parallelogram MATH

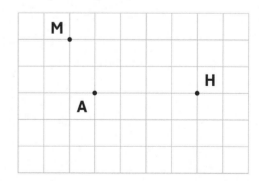

## Challenge

**5** AC and BD are diagonals of Parallelogram ABCD. They intersect at Point E. A property of all parallelograms is the diagonals intersect at their midpoint. That is, AE = EC and DE = EB.

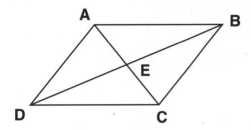

Given this is a property of all parallelograms, is this also a property of:

(a) all trapezoids? _____

(b) all rectangles? _____

(c) all rhombuses? _____

**6** In the figure below, ABCD is a parallelogram and DE = FB. Given that the diagonals of a parallelogram intersect at their midpoints, explain how you know that AFCE is also a parallelogram, without measuring. Hint: Draw diagonal AC.

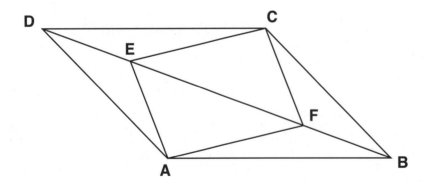

## Basics

**1** Fill in the blanks.

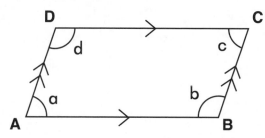

| Properties of Parallelograms | |
|---|---|
| _____ pairs of parallel sides. | AB \|\| _____ and AD \|\| _____ |
| Opposite sides have _____ lengths. | AB = _____ and AD = _____ |
| Opposite angles are _____. | ∠a = ∠_____ and ∠d = ∠_____ |
| The sum of the angles on the same side (the angles between parallel sides) is _____. | ∠a + ∠_____ = 180° <br> ∠b + ∠_____ = 180° <br> ∠c + ∠_____ = 180° <br> ∠d + ∠_____ = 180° |

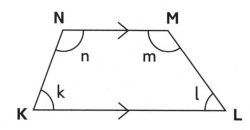

| Properties of Trapezoids | |
|---|---|
| At least _____ pair of parallel sides. | NM \|\| _____ |
| The sum of the angles between the parallel sides is _____. | ∠k + ∠_____ = 180° <br> ∠m + ∠_____ = 180° |

**2** Find the measures of ∠a and ∠b in the parallelogram below.

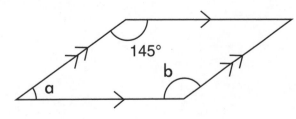

∠a = 180° − 145° = ☐°

∠b = ☐°

**3** Find the measure of ∠m in the trapezoid below.

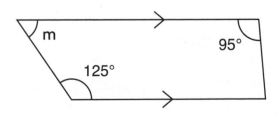

∠m = 180° − ☐° = ☐°

**4** In the figure below, ABC is a triangle and ADEC is a trapezoid. Find the measures of ∠x, ∠y, and ∠z.

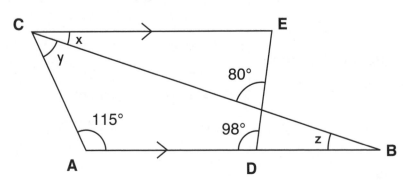

∠DEC = 180° − ☐° = ☐°

∠x = 180° − (80° + ☐°) = ☐°

∠ACE = 180° − ☐° = ☐°

∠y = 65° − ☐° = ☐°

∠z = 180° − (115° + ☐°) = ☐°

## Practice

**5** In the figure below, ABCD is a parallelogram. Find the measure of ∠a.

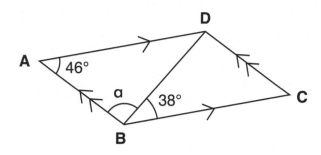

**6** In the figure below, EFGH is a rhombus. Find the measure of ∠b.

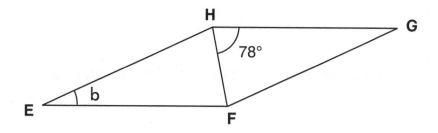

**7** In the figure below, QRST is a trapezoid. Find the measure of ∠c.

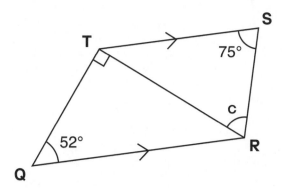

**8** In the figure below, ABCD and DCEF are parallelograms. AF, BE, AE, and DC are straight lines. Find the measures of ∠x and ∠y.

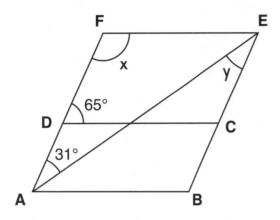

## Challenge

**9** In the figure below, O is the center of a circle and PS is parallel to OR. PORS is a trapezoid. Find the measure of ∠a.

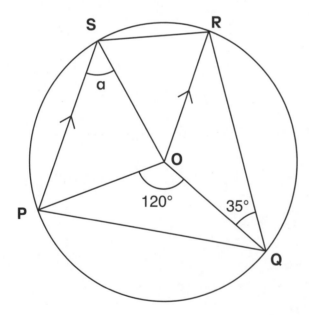

## Basics

**1** Fill in the blanks.

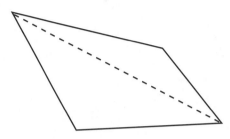 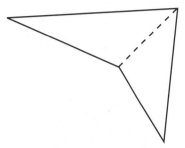

Any quadrilateral can be divided into two triangles.

The sum of the angles of two triangles is 180° + 180° = ⬜ °.

The sum of the angles of a quadrilateral is ⬜ °.

**2** Find the measure of the unknown marked angle in each quadrilateral.

(a)

52°
105°
120°
a

(b)

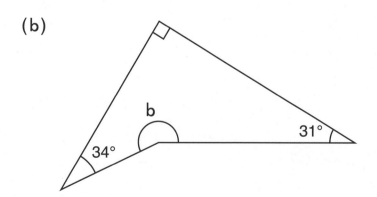

b
34°
31°

## Practice

**3** In the figures below, MN is a straight line. Find the measure of each unknown marked angle.

(a)

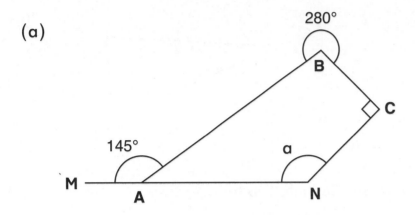

(b)

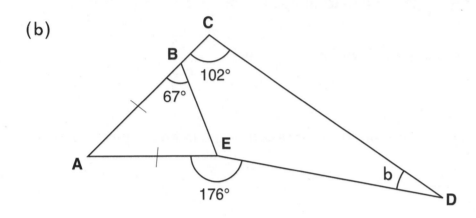

(c)

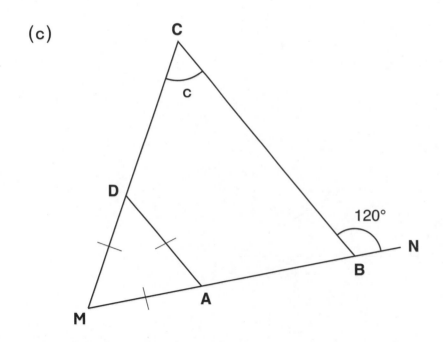

## Challenge

**4** In the quadrilateral below, ∠b is three times as large as ∠a and ∠c is twice as large as ∠a. Find the measures of ∠a, ∠b, and ∠c.

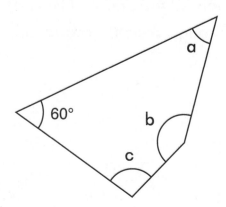

**5** What is the sum of the four exterior angles of a quadrilateral?

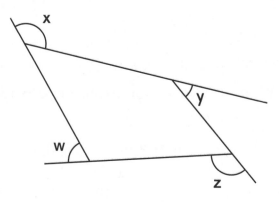

**6** What is the sum of the interior angles of a pentagon?

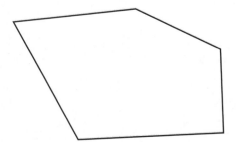

## Basics

**1** Complete the drawing of Triangle ABC in which AB = 5 cm, ∠CAB = 56°, and ∠ABC = 78°. Use a ruler and a protractor. A rough sketch is provided.

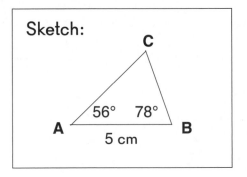

A ————————— B
        5 cm

**2** Complete the drawing of Trapezoid WXYZ in which WX || ZY, ZY = 4 cm, WZ = 5 cm, ∠WZY = 125°, and ∠ZYX = 105°. A rough sketch is provided.

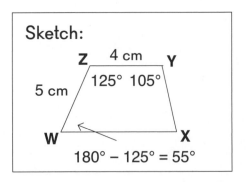

## Practice

**3** Draw an isosceles triangle DEF in which DE = EF, DF = 8 cm, and ∠DEF = 94°. A rough sketch is provided.

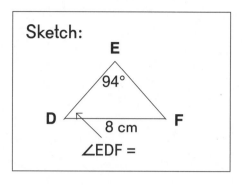

Sketch:

E

94°

D

8 cm

F

∠EDF =

**4** Draw Parallelogram PQRS in which PQ = 5 cm, PS = 7 cm, and ∠QRS = 140°. Draw a sketch first if needed.

Sketch:

**5** Draw Trapezoid JKLM in which JM || KL, KL = 6 cm, LM = 5 cm, ∠JKL = 68°, and ∠LMJ = 42°. Draw a sketch first if needed.

Sketch:

## Challenge

**6** Draw Quadrilateral TUVW in which WT and VW are both 4 cm, ∠WTU and ∠UVW both measure 120°, and one of the angles is a right angle.

## Check

**1**  Write what you learned in this chapter about the following.

(a)  The sides of a scalene triangle.

(b)  The angles of an obtuse triangle.

(c)  The opposite angles of a parallelogram.

(d)  The internal angles of a triangle.

(e)  The internal angles of a quadrilateral.

(f)  The vertical angles of two intersecting lines.

(g)  The sides and angles of a trapezoid.

**2** In the figures below, MN, PQ, QR, and SR are straight lines. Find the measure of each unknown marked angle.

(a)

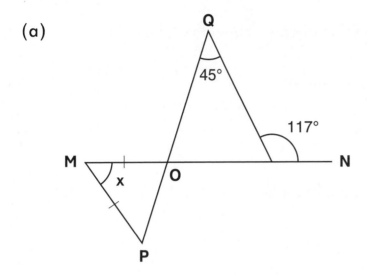

(b)

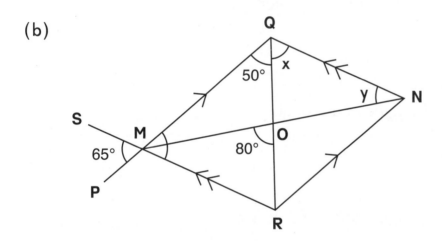

(c)

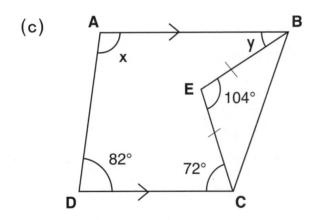

3 In the following figure, any lines that look like they are straight lines are straight lines along their entire length.

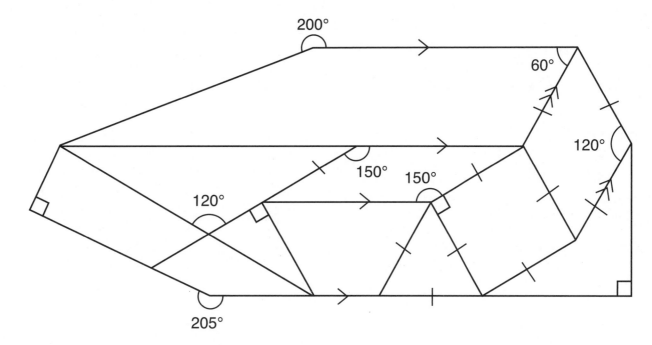

(a) Write the measure of all internal angles on the figure that are not already marked.

(b) What are the measures of the angles of the obtuse triangle? What other type of triangle is it?

(c) What are the measures of the angles of the scalene triangle? What other type of triangle is it?

(d) How many trapezoids are shown in the figure, including any that are formed by combining two smaller shapes?

**4** Draw Rhombus ABCD in which one side is 6 cm, and the angle ADB formed by a diagonal line from D to B is 55°.

## Challenge

**5** In the figure below, PQR and TQS are isosceles triangles in which QP = QR and QT = QS. Find the measure of ∠a. (Hint: ∠QTS and ∠QST equal the sum of which two angles? ∠QSP is equal to the sum of which two angles?)

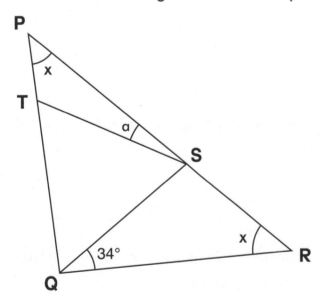

# Chapter 12 Data Analysis and Graphs

## Basics

**1** There are 4 baskets with 6, 10, 9, and 7 apples in them, respectively.

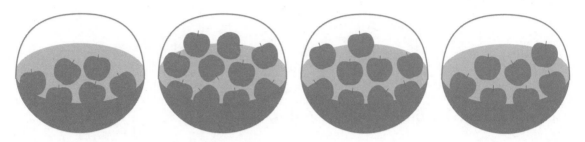

(a) Find the total number of apples.

(b) Find the number of apples each basket would have if the apples were divided equally among the 4 baskets.

(c) Distributing the total number equally among the baskets is the same as finding the average. The average of 6, 10, 9, and 7 is _____.

**2** Find the average of 32, 44, 61, 27, and 12.

| 32 | 44 | 61 | 27 | 12 |
|----|----|----|----|----|
| ? |  |  |  |  |

$(32 + 44 + 61 + 27 + 12) \div 5 = \boxed{\phantom{xxxx}} \div 5$

$= \boxed{\phantom{xxxx}}$

## Practice

**3** Find the average of each set of numbers or measurements.

(a) 35, 23

(b) 1.5 cm, 1.6 cm, 1.9 cm, 1.4 cm, 1.1 cm

(c) $7.24, $6.80, $3.75

(d) $3\frac{1}{2}$, $2\frac{1}{4}$, 3, $3\frac{3}{4}$

**4** The table shows the number of pastries a store sold each day of the week. What was the average number of pastries sold each day?

| Day | Number of Pastries |
|---|---|
| Sunday | 462 |
| Monday | 0 |
| Tuesday | 138 |
| Wednesday | 283 |
| Thursday | 130 |
| Friday | 312 |
| Saturday | 345 |

**5** The total cost of 5 meals at a restaurant was $113.75. What was the average cost of each meal?

**6** Two teams entered a math contest. The scores for the members of Team A were 98, 82, and 96. The scores for the members of Team B were 87, 91, 93, and 87. Which team has a higher average?

**Exercise 2**

## Basics

**1** Complete the table, then fill in the blanks using a heading from the table.

| Total | Number of Values | Average |
|---|---|---|
| 72 | 6 | |
| 108 | | 9 |
| | 8 | 15 |

Total ÷ Number of Values = _____

Total ÷ Average = _____

Average × Number of Values = _____

**2** The average of four numbers is 20. Three of the numbers are 9, 18, and 25.

| 20 | 20 | 20 | 20 |
|---|---|---|---|

| 9 | 18 | 25 | ? |
|---|---|---|---|

(a) What is the total for the 4 numbers?

(b) What is the total for 3 of the numbers?

(c) What is the value of the fourth number?

**3** The average of four numbers is 45.3. The average of two other numbers is 43.5. What is the average of all six numbers?

Total of the 4 numbers: ☐ × 4 = ☐

Total of the 2 numbers: ☐ × 2 = ☐

Total of all 6 numbers: ☐ + ☐ = ☐

Average of all 6 numbers: ☐ ÷ 6 = ☐

## Practice

**4** On a three-day trip, Tony drove an average of 420 miles each day. What was the total distance he drove?

**5** The average of 3 numbers is 60. Two of the numbers are 51 and 70. What is the third number?

**6** The average of 4 quiz scores is 12.

(a) If the lowest score of 3 is dropped, what is the new average?

(b) If instead a fifth score of 3 is added, what is the new average?

**7** Carlos' test scores for the last 6 math tests are 87, 97, 98, 85, 91, and 79. What score must he get on the next test to have an average score of 90?

**8** The average amount of money 5 children have is $24.50. The average amount of money 3 of the children have is $28.50. What is the average amount of money the other 2 children have?

**9** Cora's average score for 4 history tests was 88. Her average score on the first 2 tests was 92. She scored 12 more points on the third test than on the fourth test. What did she score on the third test?

## Challenge

**10** The bar graph below shows Andrei's score for 5 games.

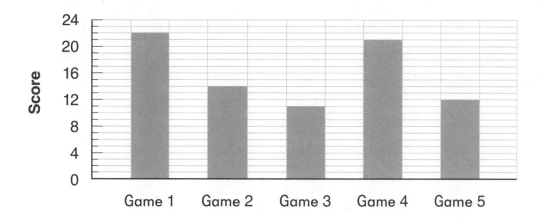

(a) What was his average score?

(b) Draw a horizontal line across the graph to show the average. By how much is each number above or below the average?

(c) Is the total number of points above and below the average the same?

(d) In a different game, Andrei's first score was 5 points below the average for four games, his second score was 8 points above the average, his third score was 2 points above average, and his fourth score was 73 points. What was his average score?

## Basics

**1** The line plot shows the height of the high jump by some ten-year-olds to the nearest $\frac{1}{4}$ ft. Express each answer below as a fraction or mixed number in simplest form.

**Height of High Jump for Ten-Year-Olds**

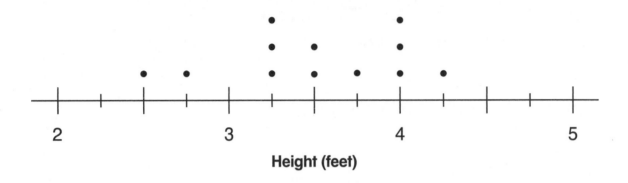

**Height (feet)**

(a) Find the difference between the highest and lowest jump.

(b) At what two heights is the data clustered?

(c) What fraction of the children jumped higher than 3 ft?

(d) Estimate the average height from the line plot, then calculate the average height.

## Practice

**2** A visitor at Yellowstone National Park recorded the duration of the eruption of the Old Faithful geyser to the nearest fourth of a minute.

| $1\frac{3}{4}$ | $1\frac{1}{2}$ | $3\frac{1}{4}$ | $4\frac{1}{4}$ | $2\frac{1}{4}$ | 4 | $1\frac{3}{4}$ | $1\frac{1}{2}$ | $5\frac{1}{2}$ | $3\frac{1}{2}$ |
|---|---|---|---|---|---|---|---|---|---|
| 2 | $1\frac{3}{4}$ | $2\frac{1}{4}$ | $1\frac{3}{4}$ | 4 | $3\frac{3}{4}$ | 2 | $4\frac{1}{2}$ | $3\frac{1}{2}$ | $4\frac{1}{4}$ |

(a) Complete the line plot.

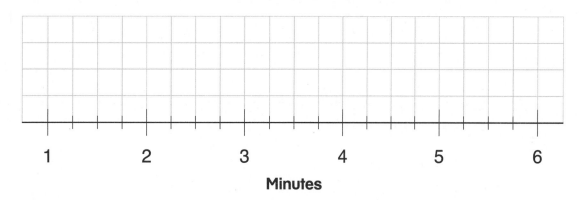

**Duration of Eruptions**

1    2    3    4    5    6

**Minutes**

(b) At which two times is the data clustered?

(c) Find the average of the 10 shortest durations and the average of the 10 longest durations. Calculate and express the answer using decimals. Then express the answers as mixed numbers.

**3** The data below shows the attention span of some five-year-olds and some ten-year-olds in minutes.

Attention span of some five-year-olds in minutes.

| 9 | 16 | 28 | 16 | 17 | 17 | 15 | 19 | 17 | 13 |
|---|----|----|----|----|----|----|----|----|----|
| 16 | 18 | 23 | 15 | 21 | 15 | 19 | 8 | 18 | 15 |

Attention span of some ten-year-olds in minutes.

| 20 | 32 | 39 | 30 | 24 | 27 | 31 | 28 | 30 | 22 |
|----|----|----|----|----|----|----|----|----|----|
| 37 | 36 | 30 | 33 | 32 | 40 | 29 | 28 | 32 | 27 |

(a) Complete the line plot, using ● for the five-year-olds and ✕ for the ten-year-olds.

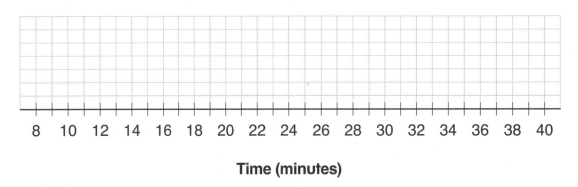

**Time (minutes)**

(b) From the line plot, what is a typical attention span for each age group?

(c) From the line plot, by about how much does the attention span increase between five-year-olds and ten-year-olds?

### Basics

**1**

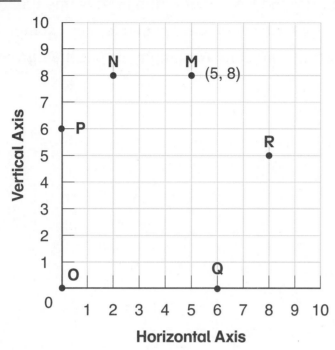

(a) On the coordinate graph above, Point M has the coordinates (5, 8). This means its position is _____ units to the right of the vertical axis, and _____ units above the horizontal axis.

(b) Point _____ is located at the origin. Write its coordinates.

(c) Write the coordinates of each of the following points.

N                          P

Q                          R

(d) Plot and label the following points.

**W** (10, 2)                    **X** (0, 3)

**Y** (3, 5)                     **Z** (5, 3)

## Practice

**2** Plot each set of points below on the coordinate graph. Join the points in order with straight lines, and join the last point to the first. Name the geometrical shapes obtained. Be as specific as possible. For example, use **square** instead of **quadrilateral**, **trapezoid**, **rectangle**, or **parallelogram**.

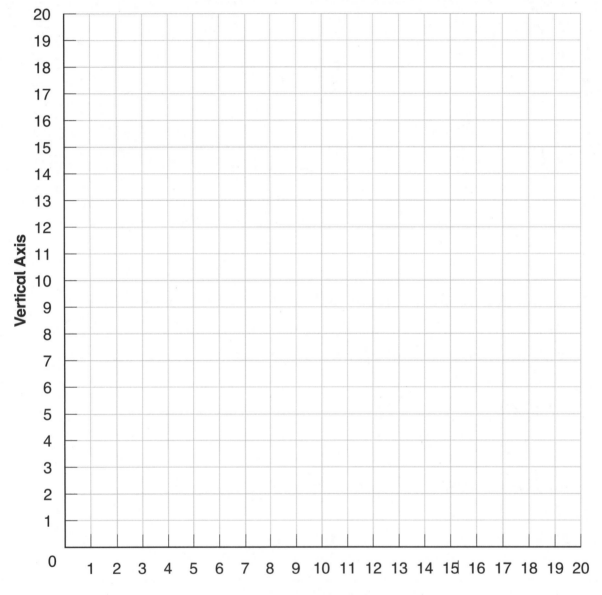

Horizontal Axis

(a)  (3, 3), (6, 3), (3, 7)

(b)  (7, 16), (13, 16), (13, 19), (7, 19)

(c)  (4, 9), (2, 12), (8, 12), (10, 9)

(d)  (19, 8), (19, 11), (12, 11), (14, 8)

(e)  (15, 15), (18, 14), (19, 17), (16, 18)

(f)  (15, 6), (16, 4), (9, 3), (8, 5)

(g)  (2, 14), (4, 20), (6, 14)

**3** Three of the vertices of a rectangle drawn on a coordinate grid are at (4, 2), (4, 10), and (10, 10). What are the coordinates of the fourth vertex?

**4** Plot the following points. Do they all lie on a straight line?
(2, 0), (3, 2), (4, 4), (5, 6), (6, 8), (7, 10)

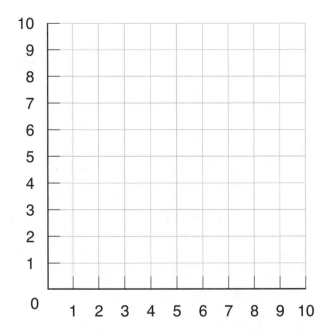

## Basics

**1** (a) Complete the table below for the side length and perimeter of equilateral triangles.

| Side length (cm) | 1 | 2 | 3 | 4 | 5 |
|---|---|---|---|---|---|
| Perimeter (cm) | 3 | | | | |

(b) When the side increases by 1 cm, the perimeter increases by _____ cm.

(c) Write the relationship between the length of the side and the perimeter of the equilateral triangle as coordinate pairs. Then plot the points on the graph.

(1, ___)

(2, ___)

(3, ___)

(4, ___)

(5, ___)

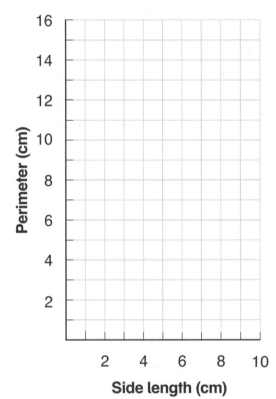

(d) Use the graph to find the perimeter when the side length is:

$1\frac{1}{2}$ cm                    $4\frac{1}{2}$ cm

## Practice

**2** For every square meter of land, a farmer needs 20 g of fertilizer.

(a) Complete the table.

| A: Land Area (m²) | 1 | 4 | | | 12 |
|---|---|---|---|---|---|
| F: Fertilizer (g) | 20 | | 120 | 180 | |
| (A, F) | (1, 20) | | | | |

(b) Plot the coordinate points for A = 1 and A = 12 below and connect the points with a straight line using a ruler. Are the other points on this line?

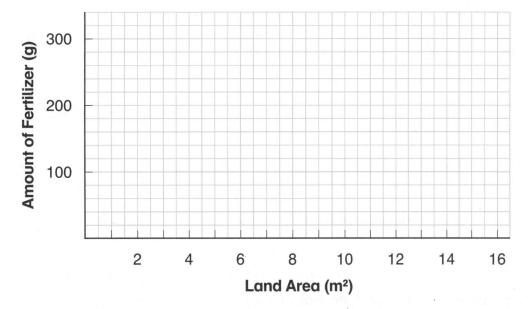

(c) How much fertilizer is needed for the following land areas?

16 m²                             $8\frac{1}{2}$ m²

(d) For what land areas are the following amounts of fertilizer sufficient?

300 g                             150 g

The graph below shows three sets of points, each set connected by a straight line.

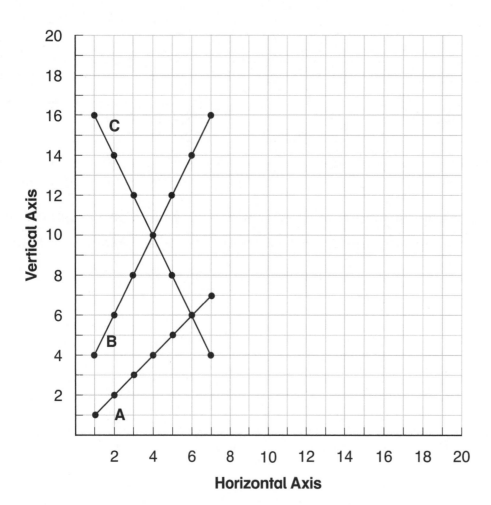

(a) Complete the table below. h is the first coordinate and v is the second coordinate for the coordinate pair, (h, v), for each point.

| h | 1 | 2 | 3 | 4 | 5 | 6 | 7 |
|---|---|---|---|---|---|---|---|
| v for Line A | | | | | | | |
| v for Line B | | | | | | | |
| v for Line C | | | | | | | |

(b) For each line, how does v change when h increases by 1?

Line A:

Line B:

Line C:

(c) Which lines go up from left to right? Of these two lines, which line is steeper?

(d) Compare lines B and C. What is the same and different about them?

(e) Extend each line to the edge of the graph. Use the graph to complete the following coordinate pairs.

Line A: (0, ___), (6, ___), (___, 19)

Line B: (0, ___), (4, ___), (___, 20)

Line C: (0, ___), (4, ___), (6, ___), (___, 0)

## Challenge

(f) The relationship between h and v for Line A is $v = h$. Write the relationship between v and h for lines B and C.

## Check

**1** Find the average of each set of numbers.

(a) 4, 0, 3, 2

(b) 2.3, 6.1, 1.2, 7.5, 6.4

**2** What is the missing number so that the list has an average of 72?

45, 78, 92, 81, _____

**3** Which two numbers can be removed from the list so that the average is 20?

12, 34, 19, 20, 24, 17

**4** A smoothie kiosk served an average of 83 customers per day Monday through Friday and an average of 128 customers each day Saturday and Sunday. What was the average number of customers served per day for the whole week?

**5** The table below shows the distance Melody threw a javelin in 10 tries.

| Javelin Throw Distance in Meters | | | | |
|---|---|---|---|---|
| 11.2 | 13.2 | 14.2 | 13.8 | 12.8 |
| 13.8 | 13.8 | 13.5 | 13.5 | 14.2 |

(a) Use this data to complete the line plot below.

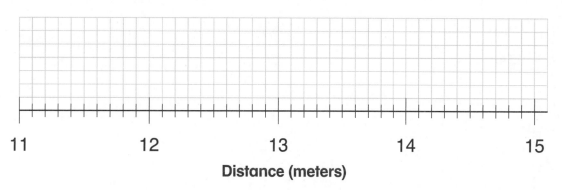

11          12          13          14          15

Distance (meters)

(b) From the line plot, estimate the average distance. Then, calculate the actual average distance.

(c) Find the average if the shortest distance is omitted, rounded to the second decimal place.

(d) How does the shortest distance affect the average?

(e) Melody's eleventh throw was her best, at 15.1 m. What is the new average of all 11 throws, rounded to the second decimal place?

**6** (a) The table below shows the distance driven at the end of each hour for a passenger train (P) and a freight train (F) on a certain railroad. Use the information to create a straight-line graph for each train.

| Time (hours) | 1 | 2 | 3 | 4 |
|---|---|---|---|---|
| P: Distance (miles) | 60 | 120 | 180 | 240 |
| F: Distance (miles) | 40 | 80 | 120 | 160 |

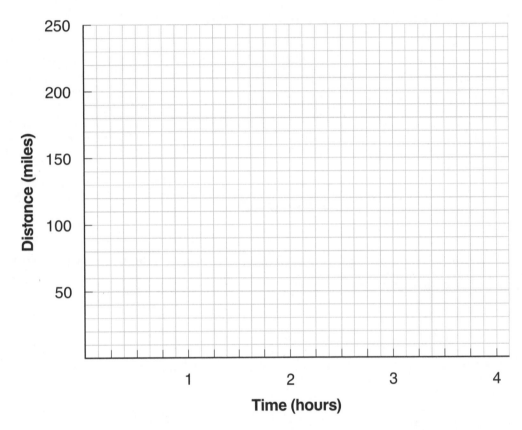

(b) How does the graph of the faster train compare to the graph of the slower train?

(c) How far has each train traveled after $2\frac{3}{4}$ h?

Passenger train:                    Freight train:

(d) By how much does the difference in distance traveled increase each hour?

## Check

**1** (a) Write the number 405,936,000 in words.

(b) Divide the number in (a) by 100. What is the new value of the digit 4?

**2** Label each arrow with a decimal.

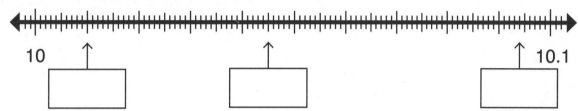

10                                                                10.1

**3** Find the values. Express the answers both as a fraction or mixed number in simplest form, and as a decimal.

(a) $2\frac{1}{4} \times \frac{1}{6}$

(b) $12 \div \frac{3}{5}$

(c) $2\frac{3}{4} - \left(\frac{2}{5} - \frac{1}{3}\right) \times \frac{3}{4}$

(d) $\left(3\frac{2}{3} - 2\frac{3}{4}\right) \div 2 \times \frac{6}{11}$

**4** Find the values. If the answer is a decimal, also express the answer as a fraction or mixed number in simplest form.

(a) 4.1 × 100

(b) 3.04 × 0.1

(c) 436 ÷ 100

(d) 74 ÷ 0.001

(e) 69 ÷ 0.3

(f) 80.5 × 0.4

**5** Multiply.

(a) 43.9 × 1.3

(b) 6.14 × 5.8

**6** Divide. Express the quotient as a decimal correct to the second decimal place.

(a) 98.2 ÷ 6

(b) 406 ÷ 1.7

**7** Debra used $\frac{1}{3}$ of a bag of sugar for a cake and $\frac{4}{5}$ of the remainder for some cookies. After that, 0.9 kg of sugar was left. How many kilograms of sugar was in the bag at first?

**8** Find the area of the shaded figure. Express the answer as a mixed number in simplest form.

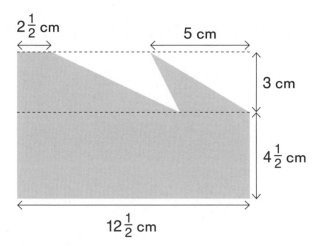

**9** A tank shaped as follows is $\frac{3}{4}$ filled with water. How much water is in the tank in liters and milliliters?

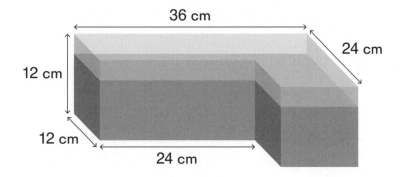

**10** In the figure below, lines MN and PC are straight lines.

(a) Find the measure of ∠PAM.

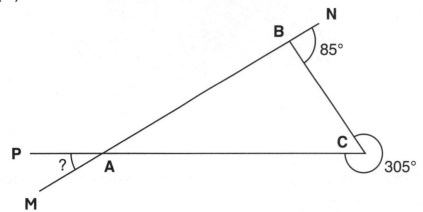

(b) What type of triangle is Triangle ABC? Classify it based on both the angles and the sides.

**11** In the figure below, AB = BD and AD || BC.

(a) Find the measure of ∠ABD.

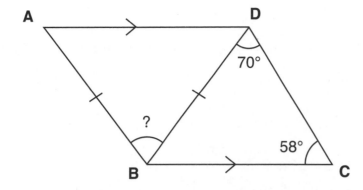

(b) What type of quadrilateral is Figure ABCD? Be as specific as possible.

**12** In the figure below, ABCD is a parallelogram. AD = DE. Find the measure of ∠EFC.

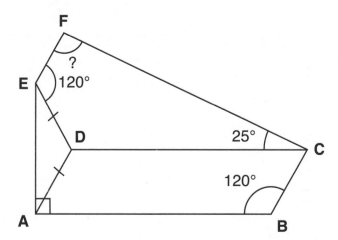

**13** Find the average of each set of numbers.

(a)  1.11, $1\frac{1}{4}$, 2.08, $1\frac{3}{5}$

(b)  $\frac{5}{6}$, 0, $\frac{1}{2}$, $\frac{2}{3}$, 1

**14** The average of a set of numbers is given. Find the missing number in each set.

(a)  Average: 17.6

17.4, 18, 13.8, _____

(b)  Average: 1

$\frac{3}{4}$, $\frac{4}{3}$, _____

**15** (a) Plot the following points on the coordinate graph, label them, and connect them in order. Connect Point E to Point A. What figure did you make?

**A** (0, 4)  **B** (10, 19)  **C** (20, 4)  **D** (0, 13)  **E** (20, 13)

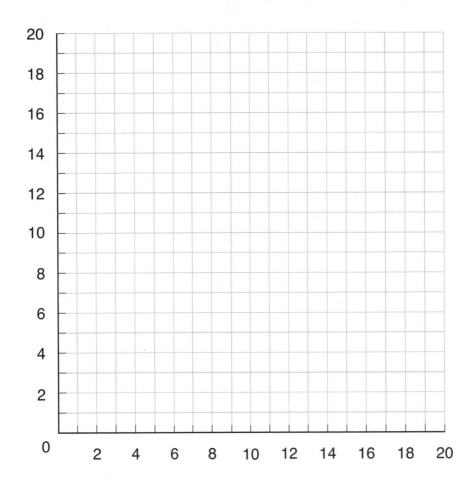

(b) Line AB has points at (2, ____), (4, ____), and (6, ____). When the first coordinate increases by 2 units, the second coordinate increases by _____ units.

(c) What is the second coordinate for any point along Line DE?

(d) Draw a line of symmetry for the figure.

(e)  What is the first coordinate for any point along the line of symmetry?

(f)  What are the other two coordinates of the isosceles triangle with one vertex at (10,19)?

(g)  What is the area of this isosceles triangle in square units?

(h)  Label Point F at (14, 13). What type of triangle is FDC?

(i)  Find the area of Triangle FDC in square units.

(j)  What are the coordinates for the intersection of lines AE and DC?

(k)  **Challenge**: How many triangles does the figure of the star have?

**16** The table below shows the relationship between degrees Celsius (°C) and degrees Fahrenheit (°F).

| Degrees Celsius (°C) | 0 | 10 | 20 | 35 |
|---|---|---|---|---|
| Degrees Fahrenheit (°F) | 32 | 50 | 68 | 95 |

(a) Use this data to create a straight-line graph for the conversion between °C and °F on the next page by plotting the ordered pairs (°C, °F).

(b) Use the graph to find the following conversions.

5 °C = _____ °F          59 °F = _____ °C

45 °C = _____ °F          77 °F = _____ °C

(c) The formula for converting between °C and °F is:

$\frac{9}{5}$ × °C + 32° (or 1.8 × °C + 32°)

Use the formula to find the following conversions.

37 °C = _____ °F          12 °C = _____ °F

## Challenge

(d) Each increase in 1 °C is an increase of _____ °F.

(e) Can you see any connection between the formula and the straight line graph?

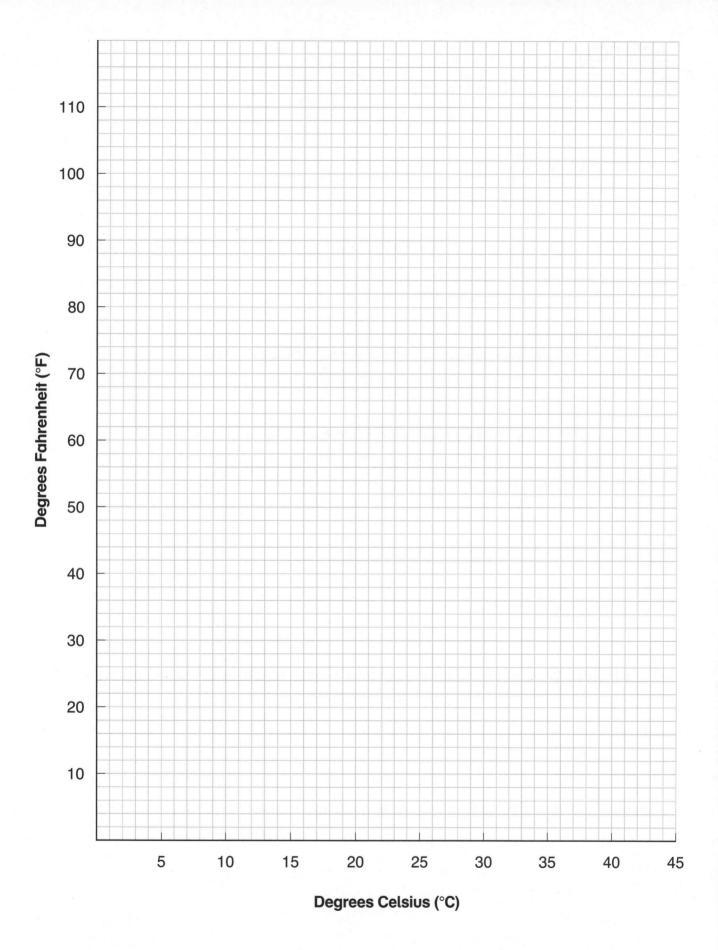

**Degrees Fahrenheit (°F)**

**Degrees Celsius (°C)**

## Challenge

 **(a)** List the first 5 consecutive whole numbers starting with 1.

Find the average.

Find the average of just the first and last number in the list. What do you notice?

Compare the average with the middle number in the list.

**(b)** List the first 4 consecutive odd numbers starting with 3. Find the average of all 4 numbers, and then the average of the first and last numbers. What do you notice?

**(c)** Test this pattern with other sets of numbers. Does it work in all cases?

**(d)** Use this idea to find the average of the multiples of 5 from 5 to 75.

# Chapter 13 Ratio

## Basics

**1** There are 2 apples and 3 mangoes in a basket.

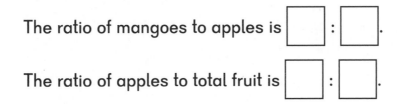

(a) The ratio of apples to mangoes is 2 : 3.

The ratio of mangoes to apples is ☐ : ☐.

The ratio of apples to total fruit is ☐ : ☐.

(b) The number of each type of fruit is doubled. Every two pieces of fruit is a unit.

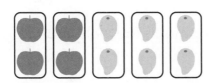

There are 2 units of apples and _____ units of mangoes.

The ratio of apples to mangoes is ☐ : ☐.

(c) 2 more apples and 2 more mangoes are added to the basket.

How many equal units of each kind of fruit are there?

The ratio of apples to mangoes is now ☐ : ☐.

**2** An apple weighs $\frac{4}{7}$ as much as an orange.

Apple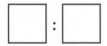

Orange

(a) The weight of the apple is _____ units. The weight of the orange is _____ units.

(b) Write the ratio of the weight of the apple to the weight of the orange.

☐ : ☐

(c) Write the ratio of the weight of the orange to the weight of the apple.

(d) Write the ratio of the weight of the orange to the weight of both fruits.

(e) The apple weighs $\frac{1}{4}$ lb. The orange weighs 7 oz.

$\frac{1}{4}$ lb $= \frac{1}{4} \times 16$ oz $= \boxed{\phantom{xxxx}}$ oz

Write the ratio of the weight of the apple to the weight of the orange.

## Practice

**3**

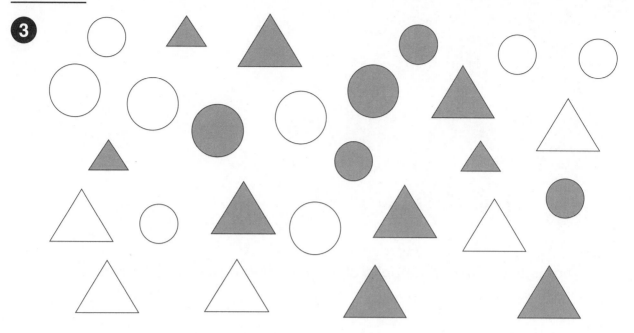

Write the following ratios for the set of objects above.

(a) Circles to triangles

(b) Circles to total shapes

(c) Shaded circles to white circles

(d) White triangles to shaded triangles

(e) Small circles to large circles

(f) Large triangles to small triangles

(g) Shaded shapes to white shapes

(h) Small circles and triangles to large circles and triangles

(i) Small white circles to total shapes

**4**

What is the ratio of the packs of 10 pens to the packs of 10 pencils?

**5** A pack of juice cans has 3 times as many cans of orange juice as apple juice.

(a) What is the ratio of apple juice to orange juice?

(b) What is the ratio of apple juice to total juice?

**6** A piece of red wire is 2 ft long. A piece of blue wire is 17 inches long. What is the ratio of the length of the red wire to the length of the blue wire?

**7** $\frac{1}{4}$ of the berries in a container are yellow raspberries, and the rest are red raspberries. What is the ratio of yellow raspberries to red raspberries?

## Basics

**1** Connor has 6 quarters and Jett has 18 quarters.

**Connor** ◯◯◯◯◯◯

**Jett** ◯◯◯◯◯◯◯◯◯◯◯◯◯◯◯◯◯◯

(a) Write the ratio of the number of stacks Connor has to the number of stacks Jett has if both boys make...

stacks of 3 with their quarters.

stacks of 6 with their quarters.

stacks of 2 with their quarters.

(b) Each of the ratios above are equivalent ratios. What is the simplest form of the ratio of coins Connor has to coins Jett has?

**2** Shade enough circles so that for every shaded circle there are 2 unshaded circles. Write the ratio of shaded to unshaded circles in simplest form.

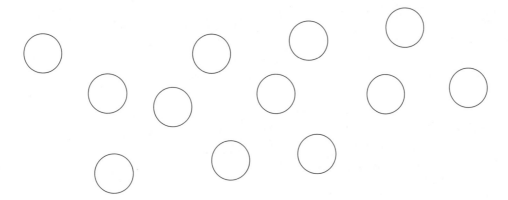

**3** To make punch, 8 cups of juice is mixed with 4 cups of soda.

(a) Write the ratio of the total number of fluid ounces of juice to the total number of fluid ounces of soda. (8 fluid ounces = 1 cup)

(b) Write the ratio of the number of quarts of juice to the number of quarts of soda. (4 cups = 1 quart)

**4** Find the equivalent ratio for 9 : 5 where the new ratio's first term is 54.

$54 \div 9 = \boxed{\phantom{00}}$

$$\begin{array}{ccc} & 9 & : & 5 \\ \times \boxed{\phantom{0}} & \downarrow & & \downarrow \\ & 54 & : & \boxed{\phantom{0}} \end{array}$$

## Practice

**5** Find the equivalent ratios.

(a) $7 : 3 = 21 : \boxed{\phantom{00}}$

(b) $4 : 5 = \boxed{\phantom{00}} : 30$

(c) $36 : 21 = 12 : \boxed{\phantom{00}}$

(d) $\boxed{\phantom{00}} : 7 = 6 : 6$

**6** Express each ratio in simplest form.

(a)  12 : 4

(b)  25 : 9

(c)  20 : 100

(d)  42 : 70

(e)  72 : 56

(f)  91 : 63

**7** Abby spent 15 minutes riding her bike and 1 hour walking. What was the ratio of the time spent riding her bike to the time spent walking?

## Challenge

**8** Which of these ratios are equivalent ratios?

| 8 : 14 | | 12 : 20 | | 21 : 35 | | 12 : 21 |

## Basics

1  The ratio of blue game pieces to red game pieces is 3 : 5. There are 48 blue game pieces. How many red game pieces are there?

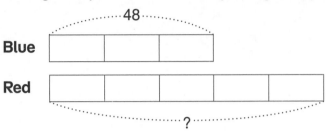

2  The ratio of blue game pieces to red game pieces is 3 : 5. There are 48 game pieces altogether. How many red game pieces are there?

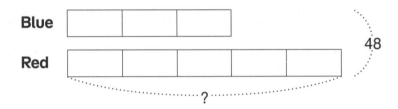

## Practice

3  The ratio of boys to girls at a party was 5 : 7. If there were 35 girls, how many children are at the party?

**4** The ratio of apple cider to soda in a drink is 2 : 3. Holly wants to make 4 L of this drink. How much of each ingredient does she need? Express the answer in liters and milliliters.

**5** The ratio of Claudia's money to Grace's money is 3 : 4. Altogether, they have $85.75. How much money does Grace have?

**6** The ratio of the length of the side of a small square to the length of the side of a larger square is 3 : 4. If the side of the large square is 28 cm, what is the area of the small square?

## Challenge

**7** A 12-ft long rope was cut into two pieces. The ratio of the lengths of the two pieces is 4 : 5. How long is each piece of rope in feet and inches?

**8** The ratio of the base of a triangle to the height of the triangle is 5 : 3. The area of the triangle is 120 cm². How long is the base?

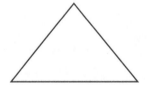

## Basics

**1** There are 12 circles, 6 squares, and 10 triangles.

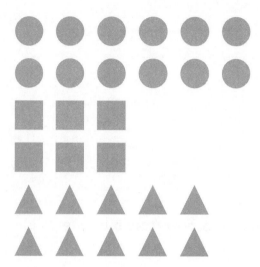

Express each of the ratios below in simplest form.

(a) The ratio of circles to squares.

$$12 : 6 = \boxed{\phantom{0}} : \boxed{\phantom{0}}$$

(b) The ratio of squares to triangles.

$$6 : 10 = \boxed{\phantom{0}} : \boxed{\phantom{0}}$$

(c) The ratio of circles to squares to triangles.

$$12 : 6 : 10 = \boxed{\phantom{0}} : \boxed{\phantom{0}} : \boxed{\phantom{0}}$$

All three terms are divided by the same number, _____.

(d) Two more squares are added and the number of triangles is doubled. What is the new ratio of circles to squares to triangles?

**2** Mariah saved twice as much money as Josh, and Cory saved $\frac{3}{4}$ as much money as Mariah. What is the ratio of Josh's savings to Mariah's savings to Cory's savings?

Josh [ | ]

Mariah [ | | | ]

Cory [ | | ]

2 : [ ] : [ ]

**3** Find the equivalent ratio for 6 : 5 : 3 where the new ratio's last term is 45.

45 ÷ 3 = [ ]

$$\begin{array}{ccccc} & 6 & : & 5 & : & 3 \\ \times[\ ] & \downarrow & & \downarrow & & \downarrow \\ & [\ ] & : & [\ ] & : & 45 \end{array}$$

## Practice

**4** Find the equivalent ratios.

(a)  7 : 3 : 2 = 21 : [ ] : [ ]

(b)  4 : 5 : 8 = [ ] : [ ] : 40

(c)  72 : 36 : 24 = [ ] : 12 : [ ]

**5** Express each ratio in simplest form.

(a)  6 : 4 : 2

(b)  100 : 20 : 80

(c)  15 : 9 : 7

(d)  18 : 63 : 27

(e)  30 : 60 : 45

(f)  32 : 16 : 48

**6** A recipe for play dough calls for 4 teaspoons of cream of tartar, 4 tablespoons of oil, and 2 teaspoons of pumpkin pie spice, along with flour, salt, and water. What is the ratio of cream of tartar to oil to pumpkin pie spice? Express the ratio in simplest form. (1 tablespoon = 3 teaspoons)

## Challenge

**7** A recipe for cookies calls for $\frac{3}{4}$ cups of butter, $2\frac{1}{2}$ cups of wheat flour, and $1\frac{1}{3}$ cups of sugar. What is the ratio of cups of butter to cups of flour to cups of sugar? (Hint: Find equivalent fractions for each quantity.)

## Basics

**1** The ratio of blue game pieces to red game pieces is 3 : 5. There are 48 more red pieces than blue pieces. How many red game pieces are there?

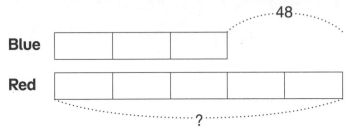

**2** Amy has $\frac{2}{3}$ as many pennies as dimes. The ratio of dimes to quarters is 6 : 5. She has 20 pennies.

(a) What is the ratio of pennies to dimes to quarters?

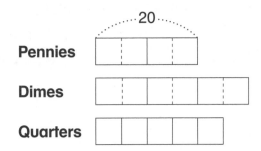

(b) How many dimes and how many quarters does she have?

(c) How much money does she have?

**3** The ratio of Mimi's money to Sheila's money to April's money was 8 : 3 : 5. After Mimi spent $98, the ratio of Mimi's money to Sheila's money was 4 : 3. How much money does April have?

Mimi

Sheila

April

$98

?

## Practice

**4** A length of rope is cut into three pieces in the ratio 7 : 5 : 4. The longest piece is 84 cm longer than the shortest piece. What was the original length of the rope in meters and centimeters?

**5** A display at an aquarium has sea stars to wolf eels in a ratio of 4 : 5. It also has $\frac{5}{8}$ as many rockfish as sea stars. There are 40 more wolf eels than rockfish. How many sea stars are there?

**6** The sides of a cuboid are in a ratio of 3 : 3 : 4. The area of the square face is 81 cm². What is the volume of the cuboid?

**7** The ratio of the area of Triangle ABC to the area of Triangle DEF is 9 : 10. What is the length of Side EF?

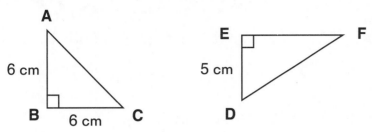

## Challenge

**8** In a fish tank, the ratio of guppies to goldfish is 3 : 5. The ratio of red-eye guppies to blue guppies is 3 : 2. What is the ratio of red-eye guppies to blue guppies to goldfish?

## Check

1  A fish tank has 7 angelfish, 12 guppies, and 6 catfish. The catfish are
   algae eaters.

   (a)  What is the ratio of algae eaters to non-algae eaters?

   (b)  What is the ratio of catfish to total fish?

   (c)  What is the ratio of catfish to angelfish to guppies?

   (d)  3 more angelfish are added to the tank. What is the ratio of angelfish
        to guppies to catfish in simplest form?

2  Find the equivalent ratios.

   (a)  $7 : 6 = 21 : \boxed{\phantom{00}}$

   (b)  $1 : 2 : 3 = \boxed{\phantom{00}} : \boxed{\phantom{00}} : 48$

   (c)  $7 : 12 = 28 : \boxed{\phantom{00}}$

   (d)  $72 : 99 : 36 = \boxed{\phantom{00}} : 11 : \boxed{\phantom{00}}$

**3** Which of the following ratios is not equivalent to the other three ratios?

| 63 : 84 | 51 : 68 | 28 : 35 | 75 : 100 |

**4** Express each ratio in simplest form.

(a)  96 : 36

(b)  75 : 30 : 60

(c)  65 : 25

(d)  13 : 41 : 7

**5** Blue paint is mixed with white paint to make lighter blue paint. Mixture A was made with 4 parts blue and 5 parts white paint. Mixture B was made with 9 parts blue and 10 parts white paint. Which mixture is lighter blue and why?

**6** The recipe for hummingbird nectar is 1 cup of sugar to 4 cups of water. Eloise has $1\frac{1}{3}$ cups of sugar. How many cups of water should she add to the sugar to make hummingbird nectar?

**7** The ratio of the average weight of male African elephants to the average weight of male Asian elephants is 30 : 13. If a group of 30 male African elephants weighs 360,000 kg, how much does a group of 30 male Asian elephants probably weigh?

**8** On Triangle ABC, the ratio of the lengths of sides AC : AB : BC is 5 : 4 : 3. The longest side is 16 cm longer than the shortest side.

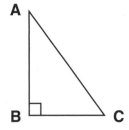

(a) What is the perimeter of the triangle?

(b) What is the area of the triangle?

**9** In an orchard, the ratio of peach trees to apricot trees is 3 : 5. The ratio of peach trees to plum trees is 6 : 7.

(a) What is the ratio of peach to apricot to plum trees?

(b) There are 126 peach trees. How many fruit trees are in the orchard?

**10** In the figure below, AE is a straight line. The measures of the angles a to b to d are in the ratio of 1 : 2 : 3. What is the measure of ∠c?

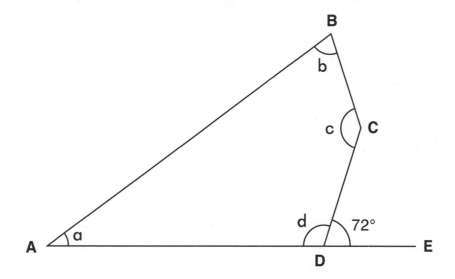

## Challenge

**11** The masses of copper and zinc in a metal alloy are in the ratio of 2 : 3. If 11 g of zinc is added, the total mass of the alloy will become 46 g. What is the new ratio of copper to zinc?

**12** The figure below is formed by two overlapping squares. The ratio of the unshaded area of Square A to the shaded area is 13 : 3. The ratio of the unshaded area of Square B to the shaded area is 2 : 1. The total area is 88 cm². What is the area of Square A?

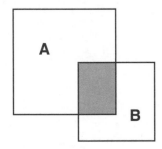

# Chapter 14 Rate

## Basics

**1** A desktop inkjet printer printed 90 pages in 5 minutes. What is the print rate for this printer in pages per minute?

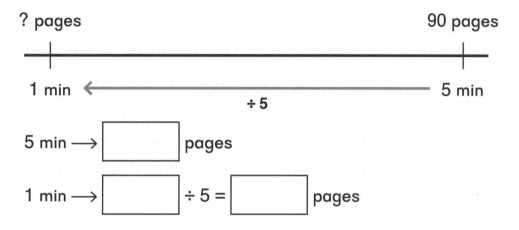

? pages                                                     90 pages

1 min                                                       5 min
                              ÷ 5

5 min → ▢ pages

1 min → ▢ ÷ 5 = ▢ pages

The print rate is _____ pages per minute.

**2** The evaporation rate of water is usually expressed as the decrease in water depth in millimeters over a period of time. The level of water in a pool dropped 6.9 cm in June. What was the evaporation rate in millimeters per day?

6.9 cm = ▢ mm

30 days → ▢ mm

1 day → ▢ ÷ 30 = ▢ mm

Rate: _____ mm per day

## Practice

**3** Mario can type 630 words in 15 minutes. What is his typing speed in words per minute?

**4** Fuel consumption rate is the average distance traveled per unit of fuel. A motorcycle can travel 210 miles on 6 gallons of gas. What is the fuel consumption rate in miles per gallon?

**5** Julien earns $900 for working a 40 hour week. What is his pay rate in dollars per hour?

**6** Emily took 5 hours and 25 minutes to run a 26 mile marathon. What was her average rate in miles per minute?

**7** Shampoo A costs $38 for a pint bottle. Shampoo B costs $9 for a 4.5 fl oz bottle. Which shampoo has a lower unit price?

## Challenge

**8** An above-ground round pool holds 11,840 gallons of water when full. It took 6 hours and 10 minutes to fill the pool $\frac{3}{4}$ full with a hose. What was the water flow rate through the hose in gallons per minute?

## Basics

**1** (a) A laser printer printed 336 pages in 12 minutes. At this rate, how many pages can it print in 50 minutes?

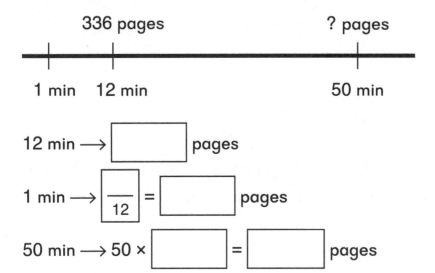

(b) An inkjet printer printed 675 pages in $\frac{1}{2}$ of an hour. At this rate, how many pages can it print in 12 minutes?

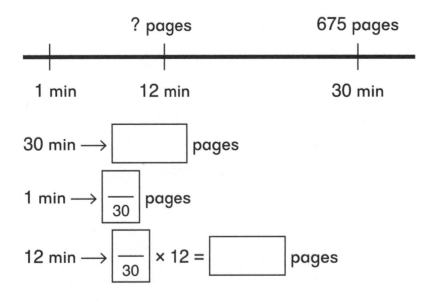

(c) Which printer is faster and why?

## Practice

**2**  A rear bike light flashes 4 times a second. How many times will it flash in 1 minute?

**3**  Jonah can walk 14 miles in 4 hours. At this rate, how far can he walk in 6 hours?

**4**  A machine can fill 400 bags of beans in 25 minutes. How many bags will it fill in 2 hours?

BEANS

**5** Carla earned $70 for 3 hours 30 minutes of babysitting. At this rate, how much will she earn if she babysits for 8 hours?

## Challenge

**6** A tank is leaking water at a rate of 1 L every 4 minutes. The tank's base measures 1 m by 90 cm and its height is 45 cm. If it took 21 hours and 36 minutes for the tank to empty, how far below the top of the tank was the original height of the water in the tank?

## Basics

**1** A car factory can produce 8 cars in 6 days, working 24 hours a day.

(a) How many hours does it take to produce 1 car?

? hours        6 days

1 car        8 cars

6 days = 6 × 24 hours = ☐ hours

8 cars ⟶ ☐ hours

1 car ⟶ $\dfrac{\boxed{\phantom{x}}}{8}$ = ☐ hours

(b) How many cars can it produce in 15 days?

8 cars        ? cars

6 days        15 days

6 days ⟶ ☐ cars

1 day ⟶ $\dfrac{\boxed{\phantom{x}}}{6}$ = $\dfrac{\boxed{\phantom{x}}}{3}$ cars

15 days ⟶ 15 × $\dfrac{\boxed{\phantom{x}}}{\boxed{\phantom{x}}}$ = ☐ cars

## Practice

**2** Kaylee can paddle a kayak 6 miles in one hour. At this rate, how long will it take her to paddle across a bay that is $4\frac{1}{2}$ miles wide?

**3** A fish market sells salmon for $16 a pound. How many pounds of salmon can be bought for $12?

**4** 50 feet of utility cord costs $12.50.

(a) How many feet of utility cord can you buy for $20?

(b) How much does 656 feet of utility cord cost?

**5** Light travels approximately 300,000,000 meters per second. The sun is about 150 million kilometers away.

(a) About how many seconds does it take light to travel 1 million kilometers?

(b) About how long does it take for the light from the sun to reach the earth in minutes and seconds?

## Challenge

**6** It takes 9 workers 10 hours to complete a certain job.

(a) How long will it take 12 workers to complete the job?

(b) How many workers are needed to complete the job in 6 hours?

## Basics

| Parking Charges at Parks-A-Lot Lot | |
|---|---|
| Up to one hour | $3.75 |
| Each additional half-hour | $1.50 |

(a) What does it cost to park at this lot from 10:00 a.m. to 2:30 p.m.?

Number of hours parked: ⬚ hours

Number of half-hours parked after the first hour: ⬚ half-hours

First hour: $3.75

⬚ half-hours ⟶ ⬚ × 1.50 = $ ⬚

Total cost: $ ⬚ + $ ⬚ = $ ⬚

(b) A driver paid $9.75 for parking at this garage. He left the garage at 5:00 p.m. What is the earliest time he could have arrived?

Cost after first hour: $ ⬚ − $3.75 = $ ⬚

$1.50 ⟶ 1 half hour

$6 ⟶ 6 ÷ 1.50 = ⬚ half-hours = ⬚ hours

Maximum parking time: ⬚ hours

Earliest arrival time was _____.

## Practice

**2** A cell phone provider charges $6.50 for the first block of 3 minutes, and $0.50 for each additional block of 30 seconds for an international call.

(a) How much does an $8\frac{1}{2}$-minute international call cost?

(b) Jasmine was charged $22.50 for calling her aunt in another country. How long did she talk to her aunt?

**3** Mimi has 2 jobs. For the first job, she is paid $13.50 an hour. For the second job, she is paid $22.50 an hour. Last week, she worked for the same number of hours at each job and earned $630. How many hours did she work that week?

**4** A delivery company charges the following rates.

| Weight | Shipping Cost per Pound |
|---|---|
| Up to 5 lb | $1.25 |
| 5 to 25 lb | $2.50 |
| 25 to 50 lb | $3.00 |
| Each additional pound over 50 lb | $2.10 |

A package that weighs 55 lb, for example, would cost $3.00 per pound for the first 50 pounds, plus $2.10 per pound for the next 5 pounds.

(a) Mattias wants to send three packages. Package A weighs 11 lb, Package B weighs 36 lb, and Package C weighs 55 lb. What will his shipping cost be?

(b) What would be the difference in cost if he combined Package A and Package B into one package?

(c) What would be the difference in cost if he combined all three packages into one package?

## Check

**1** Sonia bought a bushel of apples to make applesauce. A bushel of apples costs $30 and weighs 42 lb. There were 168 apples in the bushel. She made 12 quarts of applesauce. She used 18 tablespoons of cinnamon in all. Find each of the following rates.

(a) _____ pounds per bushel

(b) _____ dollars per bushel

(c) _____ apples per bushel

(d) _____ tablespoons of cinnamon per quart of applesauce

(e) _____ apples per pound

(f) _____ pounds of apples per quart of applesauce

(g) _____ dollars spent on apples per quart of applesauce

(h) _____ cents per apple, rounded up to the next cent

**2** A certain car can travel 384 miles on a full tank of gas. The gas tank can hold 12 gallons of gas.

(a) What is the fuel consumption rate in miles per gallon?

(b) What is the rate of gallons used per mile?

**3** 1 foot is equal to 30.48 centimeters. How many centimeters is:

(a) 1 inch?

(b) 10 inches?

(c) 5 inches?

**4** It costs $900 to tile a room that is 6 square meters.

(a) How much does it cost to tile an area that is $1\frac{1}{2}$ m by $2\frac{1}{2}$ m?

(b) How much floor area can be tiled for $200?

**5** A glacier in Greenland moved at an average rate of 324 meters per week. The typical rate of movement for a glacier is 25 centimeters per day. At these rates, how much farther does the Greenland glacier move in a year than a typical glacier, to the closest meter? (Use 1 year = 52 weeks.)

**6** Jody charges $16 per hour to babysit 1 child, and $2 per hour for each additional child. Last month he babysat 7 hours for a family with 1 child, 4 hours for a family with 2 children, and 12 hours for a family with 4 children. How much money did he earn last month babysitting?

**7** A pipe drains 250 L of water from a rectangular tank in 20 minutes. How long will it take the pipe to drain a full tank that measures 4 m by 2 m by 8 m? Express the answer in hours and minutes.

## Challenge

**8** A tank that is completely filled with water is leaking at a constant rate. At 3:00 p.m., the tank is $\frac{3}{4}$ full. At 4:00 p.m., it is $\frac{1}{3}$ full. At what time will the tank be empty?

**9** Hose A can fill a tank in 6 hours. Hose B can fill a tank in 4 hours. How long will it take to fill the tank with both hoses at the same time?

# Chapter 15 Percentage

## Basics

**1** In each of the following, the whole is divided into equal parts.

(a)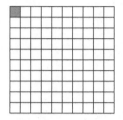

$$\frac{\phantom{00}}{100} = 1\%$$

_____% of the whole is shaded.

_____% of the whole is not shaded.

(b)

$$\frac{\phantom{00}}{100} = \boxed{\phantom{00}}\%$$

_____% of the whole is shaded.

_____% of the whole is not shaded.

(c)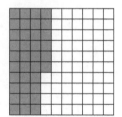

$$\frac{\phantom{00}}{100} = \boxed{\phantom{00}}\%$$

(d)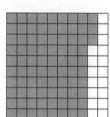

$$\frac{\phantom{00}}{100} = \boxed{\phantom{00}}\%$$

(e)

$$\frac{\phantom{00}}{10} = \frac{\phantom{00}}{100} = \boxed{\phantom{00}}\%$$

(f)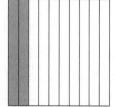

$$\frac{\phantom{00}}{10} = \frac{\phantom{00}}{100} = \boxed{\phantom{00}}\%$$

## Practice

**2** (a) Shade 52% of the whole.    (b) Shade 98% of the whole.

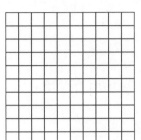    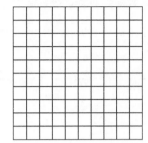

**3** Fill in the missing numerator or denominator.

(a)  $70\% = \dfrac{7}{\phantom{0}}$    (b)  $7\% = \dfrac{\phantom{0}}{100}$

**4** Express each fraction as a percentage.

(a)  $\dfrac{56}{100}$    (b)  $\dfrac{90}{100}$

(c)  $\dfrac{6}{100}$    (d)  $\dfrac{0}{100}$

(e)  $\dfrac{3}{10}$    (f)  $\dfrac{10}{10}$

**5** 89 out of 100 seats in a small theater are occupied. What percentage of the seats are not occupied?

**6** A recipe for punch calls for 7 parts orange juice and 3 parts mango juice. What percentage of the punch is orange juice?

## Basics

**1** Express the shaded part of each figure as a percentage and as a fraction in simplest form.

(a)

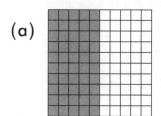

$$50\% = \frac{\phantom{0}}{100} = \frac{\phantom{0}}{2}$$

(b)

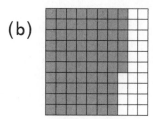

$$76\% = \frac{\phantom{0}}{100} = \frac{\phantom{0}}{25}$$

**2** A bag of 6-10-16 fertilizer is 6% nitrogen, 10% phosphate, and 16% potash. The rest of the bag contains other ingredients.

(a) What fraction of the bag is each of these three nutrients?

Nitrogen: $6\% = \dfrac{\phantom{0}}{100} = \dfrac{\phantom{0}}{50}$

Phosphate: $10\% = \dfrac{\phantom{0}}{100} = \dfrac{\phantom{0}}{\phantom{0}}$

Potash: $16\% = \dfrac{\phantom{0}}{100} = \dfrac{\phantom{0}}{\phantom{0}}$

(b) What fraction of the bag is other ingredients?

$$100\% - 6\% - 10\% - 16\% = \boxed{\phantom{0}}\% = \frac{\phantom{0}}{100} = \frac{\phantom{0}}{\phantom{0}}$$

## Practice

**3** Express the shaded part of each figure as a percentage and as a fraction in simplest form.

(a)
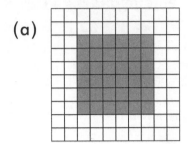

(b)
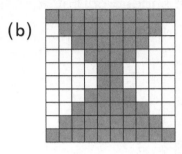

(c)
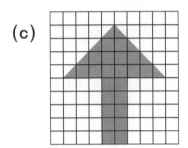

(d)
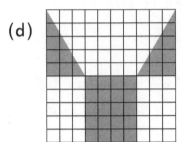

**4** Express each percentage as a fraction in simplest form or a whole number.

(a) 90%

(b) 85%

(c) 8%

(d) 42%

(e) 19%

(f) 100%

**5** Dry air is about 78% nitrogen and 20% oxygen. What fraction of the air is each of these elements, expressed in simplest form?

**6** About 72% of the earth is covered in water, and oceans hold about 96% of all of the earth's water. (Express all fractions in simplest form.)

(a) What fraction of the earth is covered in water?

(b) What fraction of the earth's water is in oceans?

(c) What percentage of the earth is dry land?

(d) What fraction of the earth's water is not in oceans?

## Challenge

**7** What are all the possible denominators when a whole number percentage is expressed as a fraction in simplest form?

## Basics

**1** Express each decimal as a percentage.

(a) $0.59 = \dfrac{\boxed{\phantom{0}}}{100} = \boxed{\phantom{0}}\%$

(b) $0.4 = \dfrac{\boxed{\phantom{0}}}{10} = \dfrac{\boxed{\phantom{0}}}{100} = \boxed{\phantom{0}}\%$

**2** Express each percentage as a decimal.

(a) $42\% = \dfrac{\boxed{\phantom{0}}}{100} = \boxed{\phantom{000}}$

(b) $30\% = \dfrac{\boxed{\phantom{0}}}{100} = \dfrac{\boxed{\phantom{0}}}{10} = \boxed{\phantom{000}}$

## Practice

**3** Express each decimal as a percentage.

(a) 0.22

(b) 0.6

(c) 0.08

(d) 0.2

**4** Express each percentage as a decimal.

(a) 55%

(b) 96%

(c) 30%

(d) 3%

**5** Complete the table.

| Fraction | Decimal | Percent |
|---|---|---|
|  |  | 87% |
|  | 0.03 |  |
| $\frac{7}{10}$ |  |  |

**6** Write the following numbers in order from least to greatest.

(a)  $\frac{1}{10}$, 1%, 1, $\frac{11}{100}$

(b)  $\frac{21}{100}$, 12%, 0.28, 2%, $\frac{2}{10}$

**7** Etienne mixed 450 g peppermint leaves, $\frac{3}{10}$ kg chamomile flowers, and some spearmint leaves to make 1 kg of an herbal tea blend. What percentage of the mixture by weight was spearmint leaves?

## Basics

**1** (a) Shade $\frac{4}{5}$ of the whole for each square.

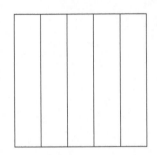  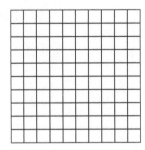

$$\frac{4}{5} = \boxed{\frac{\phantom{xx}}{100}} = \boxed{\phantom{xx}}\%$$

(b) Shade $\frac{46}{200}$ of the whole for each square.

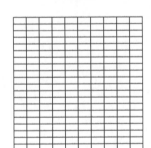 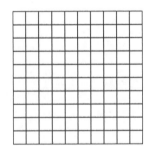

$$\frac{46}{200} = \boxed{\frac{\phantom{xx}}{100}} = \boxed{\phantom{xx}}\%$$

**2** (a) Shade the bar to show $\frac{1}{4}$ and express $\frac{1}{4}$ as a percentage.

```
|        |        |        |        |
```

```
0    10   20   30   40   50   60   70   80   90  100%
```

$$\frac{1}{4} \times 100\% = \frac{1}{4} \times \overset{25}{\cancel{100}}\% = \boxed{\phantom{xx}}\%$$

(b) Shade the bar to show $\frac{7}{20}$, and express $\frac{7}{20}$ as a percentage.

0  10  20  30  40  50  60  70  80  90  100%

$$\frac{7}{20} \times 100\% = \boxed{\phantom{00}}\%$$

## Practice

**3** What percentage of each figure is shaded?

(a)

(b)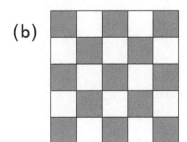

(c)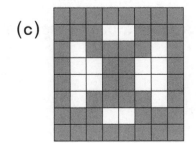

(d)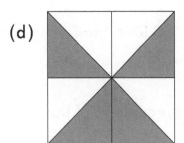

**4** The table shows the average weight of water as a fraction of total weight for human bodies at different ages. Express each fraction as a percentage.

| | Fraction of the total weight that is water | Percent of the total weight that is water |
|---|---|---|
| Babies | $\frac{39}{50}$ | |
| Young children | $\frac{13}{20}$ | |
| Teenage boys | $\frac{3}{5}$ | |
| Teenage girls | $\frac{11}{20}$ | |
| Adult men | $\frac{3}{5}$ | |
| Adult women | $\frac{1}{2}$ | |
| Men over 50 | $\frac{27}{50}$ | |
| Women over 50 | $\frac{12}{25}$ | |

**5** 105 out of 150 lawn mowers for sale in a store are electric. The rest are gas-powered.

(a) What percentage of the lawn mowers are electric?

(b) What percentage of the lawn mowers are gas-powered?

## Check

**1** Express each fraction as a percentage.

(a) $\frac{1}{2}$

(b) $\frac{1}{4}$      $\frac{2}{4}$      $\frac{3}{4}$

(c) $\frac{1}{5}$      $\frac{2}{5}$      $\frac{3}{5}$      $\frac{4}{5}$

(d) $\frac{1}{10}$      $\frac{1}{20}$      $\frac{1}{25}$      $\frac{1}{50}$

(e) $\frac{4}{10}$      $\frac{7}{20}$      $\frac{12}{25}$      $\frac{43}{50}$

**2** Express each fraction as a percentage.

(a) $\frac{75}{250}$                 (b) $\frac{135}{540}$

**3** Express each decimal as a percentage.

(a) 0.72      (b) 0.4      (c) 0.09

**4** Express each percentage as a decimal.

(a) 4%      (b) 82%      (c) 90%

**5** The table shows the average water content of various parts of the body. Complete the table.

| | Percent | Fraction |
|---|---|---|
| Brain | 75% | |
| Skin | 72% | |
| Blood | | $\frac{41}{50}$ |
| Heart | 80% | |
| Muscle | | $\frac{19}{25}$ |
| Bone | 22% | |
| Fat Tissue | 10% | |
| Liver | | $\frac{13}{20}$ |
| Plasma | 98% | |

**6** (a) Express 15 minutes as a percentage of 1 hour.

(b) Express 18 hours as a percentage of 1 day.

(c) Express 3 months as a percentage of 5 years.

(d) Express 340 g as a percentage of 2 kg.

**7** A fish tank has two types of guppies, fan-tail and sword-tail. The ratio of fan-tail guppies to sword-tail guppies is 13 : 7.

(a) Express the number of fan-tail guppies as a percentage of all the guppies.

(b) Express the number of sword-tail guppies as a percentage of all the guppies.

**8** $\frac{3}{20}$ of a one-acre plot of land was planted with beans, $\frac{2}{5}$ was planted with corn, and the rest was planted with other vegetables. What percentage of the plot of land was planted with other vegetables?

## Basics

**1** Find 24% of 350.

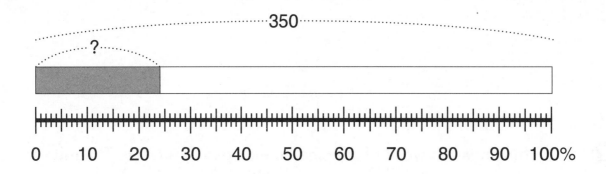

$24\% \times 350 = \dfrac{24}{100} \times 350 =$ ⬚

**2** Find 60% of 825.

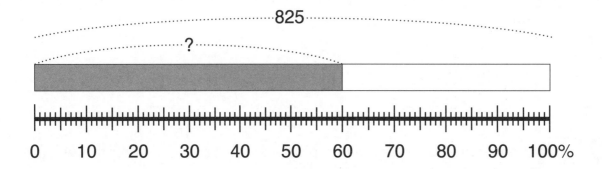

$100\% \longrightarrow 825$

$1\% \longrightarrow \dfrac{825}{100}$

$60\% \longrightarrow \dfrac{825}{100} \times 60 =$ ⬚

**3** Find 80% of 135.

100% $\longrightarrow$ 135

10% $\longrightarrow$ $\frac{135}{10}$

80% $\longrightarrow$ $\frac{135}{10} \times 8 =$ ☐

**4** How much is 82% of $35?

82% × $35 = $\frac{82}{100}$ × $35 =$ ☐

## Practice

**5** Find the values. Try to use mental calculation.

(a) 10% of 120

(b) 5% of 120

(c) 20% of 120

(d) 50% of 120

(e) 25% × 120

(f) 75% × 120

(g) 90% × 120

(h) 55% × 120

(i) 1% × 120

(j) 99% × 120

**6** Find the values.

(a) 75% of 600

(b) 84% of 25

(c) 4% × 750

(d) 95% × 120

(e) 32% × 250

(f) 8% × 225

(g) 10% × 12

(h) 72% × 55

**7** A sports store was offering a 25% discount on the purchase of any one item. Anders wants to buy a sports watch that has a price of $140. How much will he save with the discount?

**8** Chuan's meal cost $45. She paid the waiter an 18% tip. How much was the tip?

## Basics

**1** Below are 3 problems and 3 bar models. Match the bar models to the word problems and solve.

**Problem 1**

Mariah has a bag of 120 polished stones. She used 40% of her stones to make some jewelry. How many stones does she have left?

**Problem 2**

Mariah used 40% of a bag of polished stones to make some jewelry. She has 120 stones left. How many stones did she have to begin with?

**Problem 3**

Mariah has a bag of polished stones. She used 40% of her stones to make some jewelry. She used 120 stones. How many stones does she have left?

---

**Problem** _____

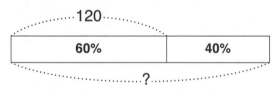

$60\% \longrightarrow 120$

$100\% \longrightarrow \frac{120}{60} \times 100 = \boxed{\phantom{000}}$

**Problem** _____

$40\% \longrightarrow 120$

$60\% \longrightarrow \frac{120}{40} \times 60 = \boxed{\phantom{000}}$

**Problem** _____

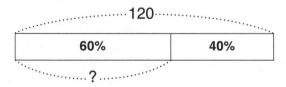

$100\% \longrightarrow 120$

$60\% \longrightarrow \frac{120}{100} \times 60 = \boxed{\phantom{000}}$

## Practice

**2** There were 75 questions on a test. Shobha answered 88% of them correctly. How many did she answer incorrectly?

**3** 10% of the parking spots in a parking lot are for motorcycles. 55% of the spots are for compact cars. The rest of the spots are for larger cars. If there are 140 spots for larger cars, how many spots are there for motorcycles?

**4** The usual price of a digital camera is $1,280. Marc bought the camera at a 20% discount and paid 8% in sales tax. How much did he spend on the camera?

**5** 35% of the books on a shelf are fiction and the rest are non-fiction. There are 15 more non-fiction books than fiction books. How many books are on the shelf?

**6** Jody earned $300 babysitting in January. In February, he earned 10% more babysitting than in January. In March, he earned 10% more than in February. How much money did he earn in all three months?

## Challenge

**7** 25% of the rocks in Mariah's rock collection are quartz. After buying more quartz rocks, the number of quartz rocks in her collection doubled. What is the new percentage of quartz rocks in her collection?

## Check

**1** Find the values.

(a) 20% × 60

(b) 60% × 20

(c) 99% × 1,300

(d) 13% × 1,300

(e) 10% of 10% of 500

(f) 30% × 60% × 450

**2** 35% of a number is 56. What is 60% of that number?

**3** 15 is 30% of a what number?

**4** The cost of a tablet was $68 after 20% off. What was the original cost of the tablet?

**5** A park has an area of 250 m². 30% of the park is taken up by a pond, and 8% of the park is taken up by a playground. The rest of the park has trails. What area of the park has trails?

**6** There are 500 red, blue, and yellow balls in a ball pit. 30% of the balls are red. There are 60 more blue balls than yellow balls. How many yellow balls are there?

## Challenge

**7** A store had a weekend sale of puzzle books. 37% of the puzzle books were sold on Saturday, and some on Sunday. At the end of the sale, the number of puzzle books left was $\frac{1}{4}$ less than the number sold on Sunday. After the sale, there were 54 puzzle books left.

(a) How many puzzle books did the store have at first?

(b) How many puzzle books were sold on Saturday?

**8** There are 500 red and blue balls in a ball pit. 30% of the balls are red. When some of the blue balls were taken out, 40% of the remaining balls were red. How many balls were taken out?

## Check

**1** What number is:

(a) fifty-four hundred thousands divided by ninety hundreds?

(b) fifty-four hundreds divided by ninety hundredths?

**2** What is the least number with three decimal places that rounds to 6.00 when rounded to the nearest hundredth?

**3** Find the values. Express the answers as whole numbers or as fractions in simplest form.

(a) $10,200 \div 600 \times 4,000$

(b) $2\frac{1}{4} \times \frac{1}{6}$

(c) $60 \div (21 - 6) \times 0.4$

(d) $12 \div 1.2 \times \frac{1}{10}$

(e) $(1\frac{2}{3} - \frac{3}{4}) \div 2 + \frac{1}{6}$

(f) $(36 - 25) \div 0.2 \times \frac{1}{2}$

4 Write > or < in each ◯.

(a) 58 ÷ 1.2 ◯ 7.1 × 6.8

(b) 3.4 × 0.9 ◯ 18.4 ÷ 6

5 Find the area of the shaded triangle in square inches.

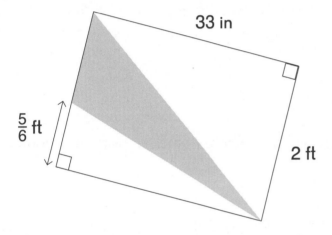

33 in

$\frac{5}{6}$ ft

2 ft

6 The solid is made from cubes. The area of the front face of the figure is 324 cm². What is the volume of the solid figure?

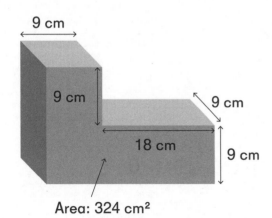

9 cm

9 cm

9 cm

18 cm

9 cm

Area: 324 cm²

**7** Plot the following points and connect them in order. Connect the last one to the first one. Find the area of the resulting figure in square units.
(2, 2), (10, 9), (4, 7), (6, 11), (2, 11)

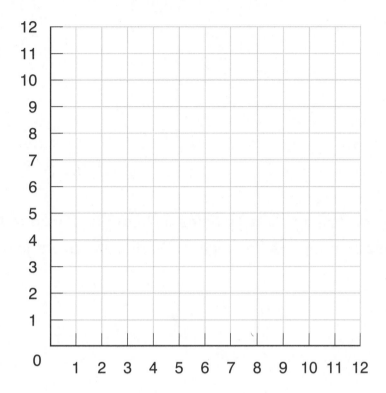

**8** Line A and Line B are both straight lines plotted on square graph paper. The coordinates for two points on Line A are (0, 4) and (8,12). Line B intersects the origin of the graph and has a point at (4, 12). Graph the two lines on a separate piece of square graph paper.

(a) What are the coordinates of the intersection of the two lines?

(b) Compete the following coordinates.

Line A: (21, _____)        Line B: (_____, 21)

**9** A room measures 4 m by 3 m. A carpet on the floor measures $2\frac{1}{2}$ m by $1\frac{2}{5}$ m. What fraction of the room is covered by carpet?

**10** Package A weighs 2.4 kg. Package B is $1\frac{1}{2}$ times as heavy as Package A. Package C is 0.75 times as heavy as Package B. What is the average weight of all three packages?

**11** The line plot shows the length of the feet of some 10-year-olds measured to the nearest eighth of an inch. Find the average length.

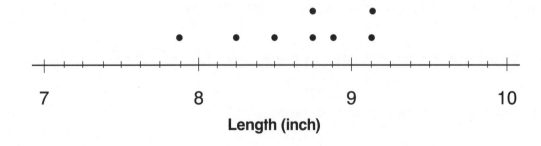

Length (inch)

## Challenge

**12** The location of a chess piece can be stated with a pair of numbers indicating (column, row). A knight moves to a new position by moving two squares horizontally and one square vertically, or two squares vertically and one square horizontally. The knight below is initially in square (4, 5). One move it can make is to square (5, 7).

(a) Write the coordinate pairs for all of the other positions for a knight after one move, starting at (4, 5).

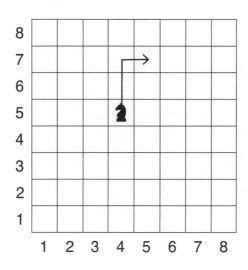

(b) What is the least number of moves a knight would have to make to move from:

(1, 1) to (8, 8)?                       (8, 1) to (8, 8)?

(c) On the smaller chess board at the right, show how a knight starting at position (2, 1) could move and visit all 8 unshaded squares once only. Then list the positions in order.

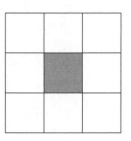

## Check

**1** Find the equivalent ratios.

(a)  $24 : 30 = 16 : \boxed{\phantom{00}}$

(b)  $3 : 6 : 9 = \boxed{\phantom{00}} : \boxed{\phantom{00}} : 12$

**2** Express each ratio in simplest form.

(a)  $52 : 36 : 28$

(b)  $20 : 12 : 56$

**3** Express each fraction as a percentage.

(a)  $\frac{14}{40}$

(b)  $\frac{405}{540}$

**4** Express each percentage as a fraction in simplest form.

(a)  82%

(b)  76%

**5** Write >, <, or = in each $\bigcirc$.

(a)  55% of 160 $\bigcirc$ $\frac{3}{5}$ of 120

(b)  75% of 52 $\bigcirc$ 52% of 75

(c)  48 ÷ 1.6 $\bigcirc$ 12% of 300

(d)  25% of 32 $\bigcirc$ 32 ÷ $\frac{1}{4}$

**6** Draw Parallelogram ABCD in which AB = 5 cm, AD = 4.5 cm, and ∠BCD = 135°.

**7** In the figure, AB and CD are straight lines. AC = CB and CE = EB. Find the measure of ∠ACE.

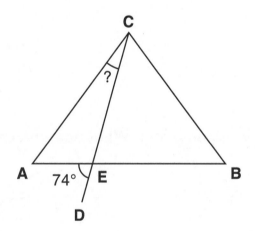

**8** In the figure, PQ and SR are parallel and SQ is a straight line. Find the measure of ∠QSP.

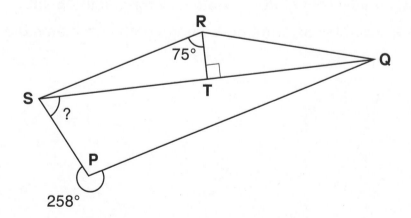

**9** A recipe for fluffy slime has a ratio of 1 : 3 for cups of glue to cups of shaving cream. How much shaving cream is needed for $\frac{3}{4}$ c of glue?

**10** The first 5 scores in a game were 25, 26, 20, 21, and 20. After the 6th game, the average score was 19, which is lower than any of the scores on the first 5 games. What was the score on the 6th game?

**11** (a) Damian got 5 out of 50 problems wrong on a test. What percentage of the problems did he get correct?

(b) On another test, he got 5 out of 200 problems wrong. If the points from both tests are combined, what percentage of the problems did he get correct?

**12** Ricardo has 45 lb of coffee beans. He wants to put 0.8 lb into some bags, and 1.6 lb into other bags. He wants the ratio of bags with 0.8 lb to bags with 1.6 lb to be 2 : 1. How many bags of each weight of coffee will he have? How much coffee will he have left over?

**13** A rectangular tank measuring 50 cm by 20 cm by 30 cm contains 3 identical metal cubes each with sides of 10 cm. Water flows into the tank at a rate of 6 L per minute. How long will it take to completely fill the tank? Express the answer in minutes and seconds.

**14** Sascha paid $102 for some 500-page reams of copy paper for her office. The next day there was a 10% off sale on the copy paper, making the cost of each ream $5.40. How much would she have saved if she had waited a day?

## Challenge

**15** Amy and Bonnie had $510 altogether. Amy spent 75% of her money and Bonnie spent 40% of her money. They had an equal amount left. How much money did Amy have at first?

**16** A group of students calculated their average score for a math test. If any one of them had scored 13 points more, their average would have been 90. If any one of them had scored 5 points less, their average would have been 87. How many students were in the group?

**17** Rope A is 20% shorter than Rope B. By what percentage is Rope B longer than Rope A?